Gold in the Blue Ridge

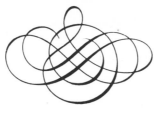

Good Hunting!

P. B. Innis

The Blue Ridge Mountains

P. B. Innis and
Walter Dean Innis

GOLD

in the

BLUE RIDGE

The True Story of the Beale Treasure

The Devon Publishing Company   Washington, D.C.

Contents

Illustrations

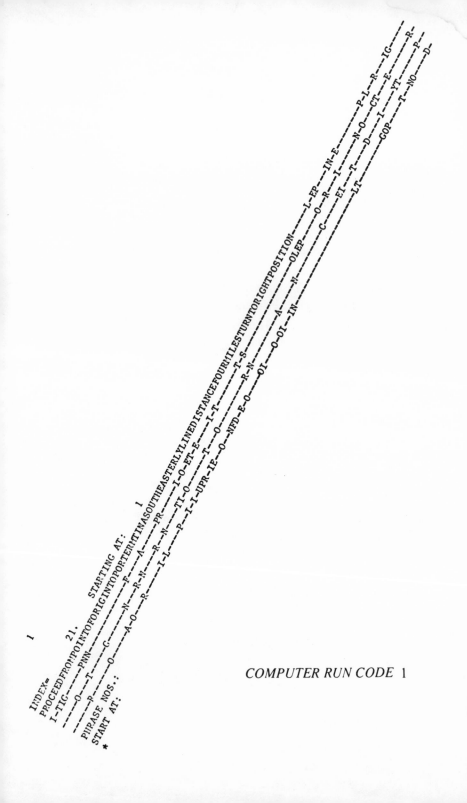

COMPUTER RUN CODE 1

RICHARD HELMS

11 September 1972

Miss Pauline Innis
The Watergate West - Apartment 1410
2700 Virginia Avenue, N. W.
Washington, D. C. 20037

Dear Pauline:

This will acknowledge your letter of
August 25, enclosing copies of the three codes of the
Beale Treasure. I am returning the copies since I as-
sume you may want them.

Also enclosed is a copy of an article from
THE WASHINGTON POST which you have doubtless seen but
which would be of interest if you have not.

As nearly as we can ascertain, no one has
yet demonstrated the ability to break the Beale ciphers.
As you are probably aware, a great many experienced
cryptanalysts have tried over the years. Of course, the
whole thing may be a hoax but we are not prepared to
state that positively.

I am inclined to think that the possibility
of finding a solution to the Ciphers would be an all-
out effort on the part of the United States Government.
There seems to be no disposition for it to become involved in such an undertaking.

I am sorry that we cannot be of more assistance.
I guess the sale of your book will have to be dependent
on your recognized skill as a writer.

Sincerely,

Dick

Enclosures - 2

Preface

Thirty-five million dollars worth of gold, silver and jewels still waiting to be dug up by anyone who can break the codes!!
Is it really true?
Are the codes authentic?
Is the whole thing a hoax?

The considerable amount of new material the authors give in this book will answer these and the many other questions frustrated treasure hunters have been asking about the Beale Treasure ever since Thomas Jefferson Beale hid it in the Blue Ridge mountains in 1819 and 1822.

In August of 1964, P. B. Innis wrote an article for *Argosy* magazine telling about this treasure and more and more people have been actively searching the area ever since. Also, there is a whole new group of treasure hunters using computers to work on the codes. So far no one has been successful.

The main reason for this is that most people are using copies of the code that contain various errors and are using a copy of the Declaration of Independence which is wrongly numbered, as the key. This was found out by the authors some years ago, but they did not realize it was so widespread until an Association started offering copies of the Beale papers for sale which are supposedly taken from the original pamphlet written by one James B. Ward of Lynchburg, Virginia. A discussion of this pamphlet and why it does not give the codes as written by Thomas Jefferson Beale appears on page 225. Another reason why treasure hunters have not been successful so far, is that they have overloked N. T. Hazelwood who is one of the key figures.

To make it easier for readers all new material and a great deal of historical background is added to the end of the original book.

Introduction

Searching for buried treasure never fails to capture the imagination of young and old. The crock at the end of the rainbow, the pirate's chest, the miser's hoard, who has not dreamt of finding such a bonanza?

No longer need treasure hunting remain a dream to be indulged in when we hear a new tale of hidden gold or a shipwrecked galleon on some far off shore. People regularly find such treasure right here in the United States: fabulous artifacts and coins in ships wrecked on the Florida coast, relics on Rogers Island, New York, a chest of gold coins found by workmen digging a ditch near the old Via Real in Texas, and artifacts found in Minnesota by Boy Scouts. Georgians still pick up coins on the banks of the Chatta-hoochee River near Columbus, and every so often news-papers report that a farmer has unearthed a small hoard as he plowed his fields.

Some of these treasures are found accidentally, some with the help of maps, codes, and ciphers, and some by a study of history and brilliant methods of deduction equal to that of Heinrich Schliemann, who discovered the treasures of ancient Troy and Mycenae.

With the great increase in the price of gold and the improved methods of metal detection and treasure hunting in general, the search for treasure is fast becoming big business. A considerable number of companies exist for the express purpose of finding treasure of various kinds on land and sea. At least three of these were formed to hunt for the Beale treasure after P.B. Innis wrote the story in *Argosy* magazine in August 1964. However, the determined man or woman working alone is just as likely to find treasure or to discover the secret of the Beale ciphers as a large company. This book gives you a head start by providing all the information the authors have gathered while actively engaged in digging for this treasure and trying to decipher the codes.

Karl von Mueller, one of the top authorities on hidden treasure says, "There are only two kinds of treasure hunters — winners and quitters."

If we hadn't quit in despair after digging all day in 1967, we might very well have the treasure in our hands by now.

Ten years ago P.B. Innis was given a copy of the Beale treasure codes by Mr. George Hart who told her that he and his brother Clayton had worked on them for many years with no success. She immediately rushed home with them, sure that she had only to sit down and work on them and the treasure would be hers in a few days. She felt even more certain of this when her husband, Walter Deane Innis, exclaimed, "I can't believe it, that's the very treasure I used to search for as a boy!" It appeared that Walter had often gone to tea at Poplar Forest, which was then the summer home of Mr. C.S. Hutter of Lynchburg, and also had camped with some other boys near the Peaks of Otter, tracing the steps of Thomas Jefferson Beale in the hopes of finding his treasure. The fact that P.B., who had come to the United States from England, should have been given the same ciphers that Walter had spent so much time on as a boy, made us quite sure that Fate had kept the *two million dollars* of treasure just for us.

According to one of the three codes left by Beale and

subsequently broken by James P. Ward, the treasure lies buried somewhere in Bedford county within a four mile radius of Buford's Tavern. The treasure, consisting of gold, silver and jewels worth two million dollars, had been hidden in iron pots in a vault six feet below the surface of the ground.

Information regarding the exact location of the treasure vault and names of those to whom the treasure should be given was explained by Beale in the two remaining codes, which no one has been able to decipher so far.

Beale had given the codes in an iron box to Robert Morriss of Lynchburg telling him to keep it safely for him. If Beale never returned to claim it, Morriss was to open it after ten years and carry out the instructions within. Morris waited 23 years before opening the box. He then was unable to decipher the codes so before his death he gave the box and its contents to James P. Ward, who finally managed to decipher one of the codes using the Declaration of Independence as the key.

When James Ward found, after a lifetime of fruitless effort, that he was unable to break the other codes, he decided to publicize the story in a pamphlet entitled "The Beale Papers."

It was a copy of this pamphlet that Mr. George Hart Sr. gave us ten years ago. The three codes had been reproduced therein and it also was shown how the Declaration of Independence had been used to decipher code 2.

We started trying to decipher the codes with great enthusiasm. We tried many documents—the Louisiana Purchase, the Star-Spangled Banner, the Twenty-third Psalm, the Lord's Prayer, Biblical texts including the first chapter of Genesis, the last chapter of Revelations and parts of the Song of Solomon—but all to no avail. We tried numbering the words of dictionaries of the day; we tried the various codes which Thomas Jefferson had devised. We also tried using the Declaration of Independence in every way we could think of, but apart from deciphering a small part of code 1, we have not had any success.

Next we decided to work on Walter's knowledge of the various caves in the area. Weekend after weekend we went down to Montvale, covering the ground and seeking out the changes in the terrain since Beale's day. At last we considered we were ready to dig and we made elaborate arrangements to hide what we were doing from any friends or inhabitants.

We flew down with a large ungainly metal detector which wasn't really welcomed aboard the plane, and took a room in the Hotel Roanoke. We were well equipped with old work clothes, but went around town separately to buy spades and pick axes, stowing them in the trunk of our rented car. Our pack held compasses, measuring rods, snake bite and first aid kits, food, and a water bottle.

We arose before dawn on Sunday morning, convinced that we were less likely to be disturbed at this hour than any other, and crept out of the hotel. We drove through the foggy darkness to the top of the Blue Ridge, hid the car and began our walk downhill carrying the tools. They grew heavier and heavier as we were not used to such labor, but we persevered.

We took turns surveying the area with the metal detector. Walter had worked out the size of the area which the amount of gold and silver in the iron pots would cover, and we hopefully plodded around and climbed over rocks, boulders and trees, holding the detector to the ground.

Suddenly the detector began to react and continued to react over an area exactly corresponding to what the gold would cover! We each tried it separately and got the same results. We were so excited we could hardly speak.

It was getting dark. Should we start digging now or wait

until next weekend and come prepared to move the gold? If we started digging now, someone might discover it and get the gold before us; better to wait until we had help and some means of transporting the treasure in safety. So we packed up and went home.

That was the longest and most exciting week we ever spent. We went over and over the names of our friends, wondering whom we could trust the most. We chose two who were strong enough to dig and lift and who could hold their tongues. Next we procured a mule and ropes and tackle and more digging implements.

This time P.B. was not required to dig—it was her job to keep watch over the mule and to make a certain birdcall if anyone came near. We found the spot and the metal detector reacted to exactly the correct area. The men started to dig. The treasure is six feet down and that's an awful lot of digging. The two friends, much younger than Walter, started off with such energy that they were quickly exhausted and had to rest. Walter went on slowly but surely, and after about seven weary hours, the spade struck metal!

Carefully we dug out bits of rock and rotted wood, then a piece of rusty metal. P.B. was told to keep a good lookout and, if necessary, lead any people far away by any means she could think of. Aching to watch the digging, she nevertheless faithfully stood at her post waiting for the treasure to be revealed. Sooner than expected, we hit metal again and slowly unearthed an old wagon wheel, the metal rim of which was what the metal detector had reacted to. Disgusted and collapsing with weariness and disappointment we called to P.B. to bring the food and water bottle and help fill in the hole.

We were all so crushed that we did something we have regretted ever since. We filled in the hole and smoothed out all trace of our presence just as any good treasure hunter should. It wasn't until about a year later that we had the awful thought that wagon wheel might have been the wheel off the wagon that the gold was transported in — the treasure might be a few feet down below it!

We raced back, but try as hard and as often as we could, we have never been able to find the wheel again. So learn from us: don't give up without careful thought, and keep maps of any likely spot in case you want to go back to it another time.

The article in *Argosy* magazine brought such an avalanche of mail that it was obvious many people were as interested as we are in finding this treasure. Letters came from all over the world, from prisons, from hospitals, from eggheads and crackpots.

To the best of our ability we answered this mail giving all possible help in the hope that by sharing experience the solution might be found. However, it became obvious that many were using the facts we gave them to sell to others and mislead them. So we became a little wary of giving additional facts from our research or knowledge handed down by Walter's relatives.

From time to time, phone calls and letters reach us saying that someone has deciphered the codes and is coming to dig up the treasure, and asking if we will grubstake them. One which arrived at midnight said, "Have broke code, but don't know if I can trust you, P.B. Will arrive tomorrow to take a look."

Another by special delivery said, "Have struck fire. Must see you. This is a big thing. People kill for less."

At first we would be nearly out of our minds with excitement, but after much wasted time, energy and money, we have become skeptical and cautious when such claims are made. As the years pass by, we are less enthusiastic about

14

digging than we used to be.

We have enlisted the help of computers as well as some of the best and most experienced code breakers of today, but as a famous code breaker told us, it is a matter of putting yourself inside the mind of Beale in the context of his time and coming up with the most likely documents which would have been available for Beale to use as a key.

The codes are classified as complex substitution ciphers of variable key system. A lucky person with a knowledge of the time is as likely to hit upon the right key as an experienced code breaker with all the assistance in the world.

We are often asked if the story is true and all we can say is that we believe it is. It's a good tale, and even if the treasure is no longer there the satisfaction and prestige attached to deciphering these codes which have baffled some of the greatest minds of our day would be sufficient reward.

The following narrative describing the adventures of Thomas Jefferson Beale and his companions should be considered as documentary fiction. Beale's character, his journey to St. Louis and Santa Fe, the manner of concealing over $2,000,000 worth of gold, silver and jewels are all facts based on documentary evidence.

We have given Beale an historical background derived from authentic documents and annals of his times. It will be obvious to the reader that dialogue has been contrived to meet events and probable communication between characters.

The maps show changes in the roads and place names since Beale's time. These were drawn by Walter Innis according to precise cartographic standards, after thorough research in the map section of the National Archives and the Library of Congress.

The Beale Narrative

1.

The horseman rode with a careless assurance which indicated his character. Named for the greatest man his parents had ever known, Thomas Jefferson Beale was an individual of versatile talent, great courage and immense determination. His easy manner belied a quick temper easily aroused by a slight or impertinence. Men seldom crossed him twice. This evening, as he rode in the shadow of the Blue Ridge Mountains towards Buford, he was in an excellent mood.

The road was good and he knew it so well that Beale let his thoughts wander over the past years. He'd done pretty well. He's come out of the war against the British with a reputation for bravery, a whole skin and a wealth of experience.

Like many a soldier, Beale knew exactly how to take up with a woman and how to let her down gently when she had served her purpose. Men liked him and women loved him and sometimes this got him into trouble. Since the war Beale had engaged in several shipping ventures which had done extremely well, but then he made the gambler's mistake of throwing everything into one risky scheme and it all but ruined him; now he found it necessary to recoup one way or another.

Beale had hoped to use his skills contracting to work on

the new University of Virginia, for which Thomas Jefferson together with 23 commissioners had just selected the site at Charlottesville. Contractors and skilled men of all kinds would be needed for the great new building. There was plenty of money to be made if a man knew how to recruit and train labor, but he could not wait for this. He needed money now.

Beale looked around the gentle valley and then up toward the Peaks of Otter where he had climbed as a boy. There was a tinge of regret in his face. He loved this land as much as he loved anything. He'd spent much of his life around the Blue Ridge mountains and he was loath to leave it but his plans were made. Tomorrow he and 29 other men were to set out from Big Lick for the western plains.

This new venture of his would bring good money and, with any luck, it could bring immense wealth and do good for the country at the same time. Beale thought with pride and pleasure of his talk the previous day with the great Thomas Jefferson at Poplar Forest, Jefferson's retreat near Lynchburg. Jefferson was generous with his time and hospitality and had willingly consented to discuss Beale's expedition into the western plains to hunt for bear and buffalo and to survey the possibility of setting up trading posts.

Emigrants were moving west. Flat boats loaded with household goods and livestock moved up the Ohio and Mississippi rivers. The people were settling along the river banks to farm the rich soil. The time was ripe for Beale's venture.

Jefferson had been enthusiastic, giving Beale the benefit of his keen mind and discussing the reports made by Meriwether Lewis and William Clark on their famous expedition of 1803 as well as later reports of such as William Clark's brother, George Rogers Clark. George Rogers Clark had

18

made a survey for the Ohio Company and later led a company of men to protect settlers against the Indians in the 1812-1814 war against the British.

Beale knew these men by reputation as they were all from this part of Virginia and he had met George Rogers Clark, a fine Virginia gentleman and a courageous soldier and explorer. Beale had high hopes for his expedition. From all accounts the Indians were settling down now that the British were driven out and the company of men he had gotten together were experienced and of good heart. Each had put up his fair share of money for the venture and there was a good reserve to pay an experienced guide and to get provisions and more equipment when they reached St. Louis.

Even if they were not successful in setting up trading posts on this trip, they would get enough skins to make the venture worthwhile. April was a good time to start, not too hot as yet and by the time they reached the mountains the snow would be gone.

It was getting dusk now, but Beale was not disturbed. He knew the road so well he and his mount could follow it in the dark. He intended to stop at Buford's Tavern to have supper and then ride on to Big Lick. Suddenly the sound of a horn blast from up the mountain echoed through the hills. There she goes, thought Beale. The coach always stopped at Blowing Rock as it came over the mountain and on this huge lump of granite issued one blast for each passenger who would be eating supper or staying the night at Buford's Tavern. This gave the innkeeper and his wife warning to set platters and send the wenches scurrying to warm beds.

Beale had tethered his horse and had drunk a glass or two before the rumble of the coach signaled its arrival in the yard. He was curious to see who was traveling so he got up and went to the door. With the usual noise and bustle the door of the coach was opened and the steps let down. It was getting dark now, but Beale could see the first passenger out of the coach was a heavy set man named Davenport who Beale knew spent most of his time buying and selling slaves. Behind him was a thin, tired looking man followed by a beautiful young woman. Beale knew from his shipping ventures that this must be Robert Morriss and his wife, who had lost money on their ships and now had established a hotel in Lynchburg. They had been so highly spoken of that Beale desired to meet them.

Next morning Beale and the rest of the company were saddled up and ready to ride from Big Lick about eight. A crowd of friends and relatives were there to see them off. It was a noisy, boisterous send-off. Each knew the danger of the trip, but none put into words the fear that they might never see them again. Wives and children clung tearfully to the men, making Beale all the more thankful that he had kept free from marriage. Then, cutting short the farewells and good wishes, Beale gave the signal, "Ho, Westward Ho," and they were off in a cloud of rising dust.

2.

Once on their way neither Beale nor any of his company looked back. They had planned and worked on this expedition for almost a year and they would let nothing stop them now. They intended to reach the western plains or die in the attempt. Apart from the urge to hunt, the spirit of exploration was in the air. The great lands of the Louisiana Purchase stretching in a band from the Canadian border down to the Gulf of Mexico, although purchased in 1803, had not yet been fully explored. Lewis and Clark had covered the northern parts in the years between 1804 and 1806, and Zebulon Pike had traveled as far as the Rocky Mountains and on to Santa Fe, but the hordes of emigrants who were later to people these lands had not gotten this far. The tales of what the explorers had seen and endured served only to inflame the desire of the men to go and see for themselves.

Thomas Jefferson, perhaps envisioning a future nation stretching from Atlantic to Pacific, had taken a personal interest in arranging the expeditions of Lewis and Clark and Pike. Beale therefore had sought the great former President's advice and help for his own expedition.

Britain, Russia, Spain, France and Mexico all laid claim to much of the lands, and were particularly jealous of their trading rights. Spain refused passports to American traders and Beale knew that the passports granted to Lewis and Clark by foreign governments specifically mentioned that they were on a scientific expedition and that they carried with them no trading goods other than gifts for the Indians. Beale's whole company knew that once they were beyond St. Louis, any mention of trading could land them in prison. Their thoughts were not on the dangers, however, but rather on the excitements and rich rewards that lay in the unknown lands.

They intended to ride directly to St. Louis, obtain a guide and equipment and then move on so that they could spend the greater part of their time beyond the frontier. They followed the age-old path of the buffalo, made when the great beasts came to drink at the mountain springs. The Indians followed this same trail when they came from the west to summer near the Peaks of Otter. Now the feet of the white man and his horses were treading it. Soon their wagon wheels would grind it into a pathway of death for the Indian and the buffalo, but as Beale and his men rode west, the buffalo still roamed and the Indian still hunted him, neither aware of his fate.

For a while they rode on through landscape that did not change much, for the land was still hilly. The trees were coming into full leaf, the white flowers of the service berry, starwort and other wild flowers made spots of color among the trees. The country was abundant with life. The sounds of birds and small animals were all around them.

Most of the company, like Beale, had served in the army and thus could settle immediately into the routine of camp life. There was a certain amount of inherent discipline in the company which made Beale's task as leader much easier.

Game was so abundant that they had no trouble keeping the cooking pots full. The wild turkeys were particularly good and the deer were plentiful. They saw no bear for a while; this did not surprise them as it was early for bear to come out of hibernation, although they saw an occasional sleepy mother and her cubs cautiously emerging from a cave. Some days they made excellent progress because the trail was pretty well used and easy to follow; other times they had to chop their way through dense undergrowth or move great boulders out of the way before the horses could pass. But it wasn't until they were 12 days out of Big Lick that they saw any Indians. They were making camp that night in sparsely settled country. It was a little more open than that behind them but there were clumps of trees and the land was rolling. The cooking pots were just about ready when one of the guards gave the alarm and amid the terrified neighing of a horse a shot rang out and a shower of arrows hit the camp.

Immediately Beale grabbed his gun and was by the side of the guard. They could see no one, and no more arrows fell.

"They were after the horses. I saw them sneaking up and fired at them."

"Did you get anyone?"

"I don't know. I don't think so—the light's too bad."

"That's lucky for us. They'll probably wait 'til morning to try again."

The men had all taken up positions around the camp. Using some of the baggage for protection they covered the landscape with their guns in every direction. Itching for action, they were disappointed when nothing happened. It was too dark for pursuit and unlikely that the Indians would attack again before morning, so a double guard was set and they bedded down for the night with guns and ammunition beside them.

Beale thought, from what the guard had told him, that the Indians were after their provisions or horses, and not likely to attack because the company outnumbered them. Chances were that they would sneak up again during the night or early morning to try to get what they could. They would prefer horses, but a scalp or two would be better than nothing. Beale could not sleep. He made the rounds of the little camp, checking the guard and adding several more men to guard the horses. But all was quiet and it wasn't until daylight that the relief watch reported smoke rising to the left of them. Smoke could come from a settler's cabin, but this was too much to be coming from one chimney. It was too heavy to be a smoke signal of the Indians.

"Looks like fire to me. Maybe those Indians set fire to a cabin. There's one or two settlers around these parts," the guard reported to Beale.

To Beale and his men nothing could be worse than to settle in such a place, tied to the piece of land out of which they had to wring their sustenance. But to the men and women living in them, each cabin represented the fulfillment of a dream. Even though they had to protect themselves against Indians, sickness and loneliness, they never would give it up.

"Did you see anything?" Beale asked.

"No, just noticed the smoke when it got light. Could've been there yesterday without us seeing it. It was getting dark when we made camp and the lie of the land would have kept it out of sight."

"Could be a settler burning off his land?"

"Not enough smoke for that and too much for a chimney—must be some poor devil's home them Indians have got."

The men were in favor of striking camp as soon as they had eaten something and attended to horses. Soon they were on their way, guns across the saddle, to see if anyone needed help. The trail took them near the smoke which seemed to be dying down. There was no sign of the Indians but they were all alert for every sign or rustle.

24

Beale called a halt and was consulting with some of the men when he saw a movement in the underbrush. Expecting an arrow through his body, he fired a quick shot. A terrible high pitched screaming came tearing into the air. Beale was out of the saddle pushing the brush aside in a moment. An open, agonized mouth in a blood stained face stared up at him. A white face! A woman's face! The screaming grew louder.

"God! it's a white woman!" Two of the men had joined Beale and were gazing in horror at the cowering blood-stained figure lying on the ground.

"Get Joe, quick." Joe was a man who'd had a good deal of experience with the wounded in the war of 1812. His re-assuring manner with the sick calmed them and helped them in their pain.

"There, now, hush," Joe said to the woman, "I'm not going to hurt you. Let me see where the damage is." He motioned the men back and all but Beale moved away. He was holding the brush back so Joe could see and get to the woman. The screaming went on and on.

"Get me some water so I can wash off this blood and see where she's hurt," Joe said. He was afraid to move her until he found out where she was injured. She was lying on her side turned away from him to the earth, her knees up and her bloodstained face hidden now. Joe turned her over, revealing a bloody mass within her bodice.

"No, no," the poor woman screamed as he lifted her hands from it. For a moment Joe could not tell what the mass was and then he saw it was a tiny baby, its head smashed by a hatchet. Joe let the woman's hands go back over the bloody corpse. But he took a piece of cloth out of the box of medical supplies he had brought with him and dipped it in the water one of the men had brought, and carefully tried to wipe the blood off her face.

25

The cold water had some effect on her—the screams turned to moans and she closed her eyes tremulously. They were relieved to find that her face was not injured. The blood was from the baby.

"I can't tell about her chest," Joe said to Beale, "but the rest of her seems all right. I don't think you hit her; it was just fright that started her screaming."

"Thank God!"

Joe raised the woman up and gave her a sip of brandy.

"Now, ma'am, are you hurting any place? We want to help you, but you've got to help us too."

The woman stared at him vacantly, clutching the dead baby to her bosom. Beale felt a tremendous anger against those who had done this. The woman was young, little more than a child. Her husband was most likely killed and her cabin burned. What would become of her?

"Where's your home," Joe asked, "we'll try to take you there."

The woman stared at him, murmuring, "Home, home." Then she said, "It's gone. They burned it—the Indians came yesterday." Then she started weeping with such terrible desolation that, although hardened to such sights from the war, Beale and his men felt lumps rise in their throats.

"Do you have any friends we could get you to, ma'am?"

"I don't know, they're most likely dead too—but my baby, can you help my baby?"

"Let's get you to some place. I can't tend to the baby here," Joe said.

"Well, there's Mrs. Evans—she was our nearest neighbor—but I don't know what happened to her, they came so fast."

"Are they gone?"

"I don't know. I couldn't find Dan. They were all yelling and shouting and the house was burning and they took my baby but I got her back and then I ran and ran until I couldn't run no more and I hid myself here until you started shooting. I've been here all night." And she started sobbing again.

"Did you get hit when the gun went off?" Joe asked.

"No, it was over my head but it scared me awful."

The woman was quiet now and so Beale motioned to one of the men to take place holding the brush back. Three men went ahead to see if all was clear and then they all followed carrying the woman in a litter made from a blanket tied across two poles.

The cabin was still smouldering. The smoke they had seen must have been caused by some roof logs falling in. They moved cautiously, alert for stray Indians, but there was no movement.

"Dan, I'm here, Dan," the woman started calling in a frightened voice.

"Where do you think he is?" she asked. "It's not like him to go far away. Do you think he's out looking for me?"

"He could be, there's no way of knowing," Beale answered. "Where's that neighbor located? We could see if he's there."

The woman looked vacantly around as if she had never seen the place before. "I don't know, I've forgot. It's that way I reckon." She pointed behind the cabin.

"We can't leave her here, that's for sure. We'd better go find that neighbor." They were about to ride on when a man emerged from the woods behind the cabin. Beale went out to meet him. He looked exhausted but he managed a smile.

"Glad to see you. I'm Will Thomas. I came over to see what happened to Dan and Nellie."

"She's not hurt, but the baby's dead. She keeps holding on to it. She says she doesn't know what happened to her husband. There's nobody here, so there's a chance he's out looking for her."

"Unless they carried him off."

"Might have," Beale said, "have they gone?"

"Yes, I watched them go. About twenty there were. Lucky they didn't come near us."

"Is there anyone to take care of her? Someone's got to do something about that baby. It's a woman's job."

"Well, I don't know that she has any relations around."

"She spoke about a Mrs. Evans. Do you know her?"

"She's a right good woman and her place isn't far from here. She's a widow woman, but she's got a good place. Me and my wife and the four young 'uns have to make do with a couple of rooms until I build more. She'd be better off with Mrs. Evans."

Nellie did not protest when Joe told her they were going to take her to Mrs. Evans.

"Will Thomas is here and he'll show us the way."

"Is Dan there?"

"We don't know, but it's likely he'll look for you there."

In case there were any Indians around still, ten men went with Will Thomas and Nellie. Beale and the others stayed near the cabin. This is no life for a woman, Beale thought, and was again glad that he had no wife. While they waited for the men to return, they did what they could around the place. The cow in the shed needed milking and they found some corn which they threw to the few chickens scratching in the yard. Nothing was left of the house or the furnishings.

Beale was relieved when Will Thomas came back with the men and said that Mrs. Evans' place was safe and that she would take care of Nellie. Meanwhile he would see to it that the cow and chickens were taken care of.

Beale liked the look of Thomas. He was a simple, hardworking man whom Beale felt could be trusted, so he gave him a couple of gold pieces for Nellie as well as the blanket they had carried her in, so that she and Dan would have something to start again. Then he gave Thomas some flour and meal for himself.

The man was touchingly grateful. Such things were scarce at this time of the year.

They rode away leaving Thomas standing in front of the ruins of his friend's home. What would become of them, Beale wondered. There were not enough settlers in the area to stand against the Indians, but they didn't seem disposed to move back. The government gave them little or no protection; they had to rely on themselves.

Nellie and her murdered baby were on the minds of most of the men, and each was silently demanding that Providence send her husband back safe and sound. They were well used to the tragedy of life but somehow they were still touched by the suffering of women and children on the merciless frontier. But there was nothing more they could do and, in a few days, Nellie slipped into the dim corners of their memory where, of necessity, the tragedies and horrors of life were hidden.

The days passed and the landscape changed as they moved into less hilly country. The going was easier now as the woods were not so dense. They met with no serious trouble with Indians. One band harassed them for days but swore eternal friendship after Beale feasted them and gave them presents. The worst mishap they had was the loss of one of the pack horses who had to be shot after he broke a leg while fording a river.

By May 7 they sighted St. Louis and knew that the first part of their journey was accomplished.

3.

In 1817 St. Louis was a town of about 3,000 people situated on the banks of the Mississippi river. It was the territorial capital and the center for extensive trade with the Indian tribes along the Mississippi and the Missouri rivers. The St. Louis traders completely monopolized the fur trade with the Osage Indians and many large fortunes were made here. The population, mostly Roman Catholic, was a mixture of French, Spanish, English and Indian.

At this time of the year St. Louis was a noisy, bustling place; the rough voices of trappers just in from the mountains, the grunts of the Indians mingling with the French accents of the early families, many of whom had been in St. Louis since its founding in 1763. It did not take long for Beale and his company to find satisfactory accommodations for themselves and their horses on the Rue Royale. St. Louis was a supply point for traders, hunters and explorers, so there was an assortment of inns and boarding houses.

After settling in, Beale went to call on Pierre, a prominent trader to whom he had a letter of introduction. Monsieur Pierre was a shrewd but scrupulous trader in furs and he had a comprehensive knowledge of the territory, the trade, the people and the animals and knew all the best guides personally. A small, dark man with a sallow complexion, his bright, sharp eyes missed nothing; he was known as chief of the hunter and the hunted.

"So, you want to go to Santa Fe and hunt in the desert plain, do you?"

"Yes, we thought . . ."

"Do you know that even if you are fortunate enough to reach Santa Fe, the governor may not let you in, or if he does, he could very well have you thrown in the dungeons?"

"I had heard that traders were not welcome in Santa Fe but I thought travelers and hunters might be."

"They might be, but it's a risk. It's a terrible journey— some of the worst terrain I know. There's plenty of buffalo and bear around these parts, no need to go so far."

But when he saw that Beale was set on going to Santa Fe, Pierre agreed to find a good, trustworthy guide and to help with their outfitting.

"Where are you staying?" he asked. "I may be able to get hold of the guide I have in mind for you and send him over."

"I'm at the Hunter's Tavern," said Beale. "We are only staying long enough to get a guide and equipment and then we get on the trail again."

Monsieur Pierre nodded, then he said, "For the sake of my friend who sent you to me, I feel I should dissuade you. The hazards are too great. Have you ever seen the desert area?"

"No, I know nothing of it, but with a good guide we can cross it. It has been done before."

"Yes, but many more have died in the attempt than have crossed it. The Indians of these parts are quite different from those in the east. They are great horsemen and swoop down on the traveler, laying him low before he can lift his rifle. They fight with lance and spear eminently suited to their type of warfare and to the terrain. There is no escape from them and no means of pacifying them when they are intent on war."

"We are good horsemen and well used to Indian fighting."

Pierre looked at him sadly. "I see that I make no impression on you. The Indians of your country fight on foot. You have the trees and shrubs for concealment. They scalp and kill and burn, but the Indians of the desert plain are masters of the most horrible tortures. They can keep a man alive for weeks through tortures that leave him scarcely recognizable. Torture is their main entertainment. You are but 30 men. You will be out there with mile upon mile of open desolate land around you, exposed to the elements as well as the Indians. There is no shade from the sun and no shelter from the wind. It is not meant for you, Mr. Beale, only for savages and animals."

"I intend to make the journey regardless of the hardships, but I thank you for your warnings. Can you give us any advice on dealing with them?"

"Good fortune and a good guide are the best precautions. A good guide is likely to know the movements of the Indians and all the needs of the journey. It would be wise to learn what you can of the ways of the Indians yourself. The Wichitas, the Apaches and the Comanches are those you are most likely to meet on the route to Santa Fe. Good fast horses are of the utmost importance. Even the most savage warrior will lose heart if he thinks his horse is outclassed by his enemy."

"This guide you have in mind for me, will he be able to advise me on all this?"

"Yes, he is the best available, but you will have to persuade him to take you. Not only is he expensive, but he insists the expedition be well equipped, and he has to approve the men and horses also."

Beale looked annoyed. "Is he an Indian?"

"Yes, but he has been with white men so long that he speaks good French and English. He is no longer young and has enough money to last the rest of his life so he can pick and choose the company he guides. Also his life is at stake with yours, you know."

"That's true, and if he's the best we'll pay the price."

"I will guarantee that any guide I find you will earn his pay."

It wasn't until three days later that Beale was visited by Hawk Eye, who said he was sent by Monsieur Pierre.

"You need guide for Santa Fe? I am the best." He didn't look it. He was certainly no longer young. In fact he looked like a mummy recently dug up, his skin was so wrinkled and leathery. Beale doubted if he had the strength to go 50 miles let alone the 800 or more to Santa Fe.

"I need the best as none of my company has made the journey."

"I the best." The black eyes looked impassively at Beale, then he said simply, "You are best, white man. I take you to Santa Fe."

To Beale's everlasting surprise, Hawk Eye's acceptance of him had a reciprocal effect. He found himself accepting Hawk Eye as the best guide in America and he was prepared to trust him with his own life and the lives of his men without further question.

Hawk Eye's demands were high. He insisted on purchasing fresh horses and vast amounts of supplies. "You not sorry, these faster than Indian horses, no food part of journey, must take with us."

The men complained bitterly about the added expenditure. "That Indian's out for all he can get. What do we want with all those extra horses? And we've got enough provisions

34

for an army. He's in the trade and making plenty out of this."

They also began to talk of the dangers of the journey. Tales of the horrors of the desert and the Indian tortures were told in the bars at night. Some were having second thoughts about the trip.

Hawk Eye seemed to know everything and he spoke to Beale warning him about the doubts of some of the men. He wanted Beale to send away any of the men whose heart was not in the trip, since a half-hearted man could bring ruin to them all. "Make like American army. One leader, all obey. Kill if not obedient to leader. Only way to Santa Fe."

After some thought Beale saw the wisdom of Hawk Eye's remarks and he called the company together and advised them of all the risks as detailed to him by Monsieur Pierre. Then he took a vote as to whether they go on to Santa Fe or hunt in the areas near St. Louis. All voted to go on, unanimously elected Beale as leader and swore to obey the rules of the expedition.

On May 17, 1817 Beale and his company set forth from St. Louis across the unknown, unexplored territory, destined for Santa Fe.

The Beale route to Santa Fe

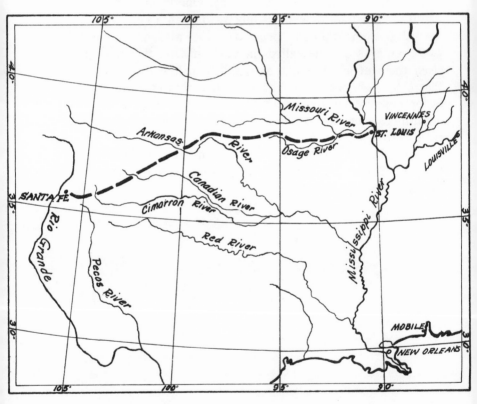

4.

When the company left St. Louis Hawk Eye followed the Missouri river to what is now Independence and, although the going was hard, they had been so prepared for something worse that the men began to think the hardships were exaggerated.

Then suddenly the world changed. The trees were gone and ahead of them stretched a terrible, open endlessness of grass. On and on and on it went, farther than they could see. There was a movement in it, a rolling sensation like the unquiet heaving of the sea. The sun beat down and there was nothing to cast a shadow, only themselves and their horses.

Beale reined in his horse and they were all still as if they were part of the immensity. No one spoke. They had no words for this. This was something they, from another smaller world, had never seen. They were awed by it.

Hitherto the land had showed itself decently clothed in trees and plants and flowers. Here it was stripped of all such finery. Here it was naked and stark, its contours bared to the eye and touch of man. It was too much to comprehend. Beale had never expected this revelation of things beyond his experience. What other unknowns might lie ahead?

"Do not move too fast," Hawk Eye cautioned. "There is much land to cross."

"Does this place have a name?" Beale asked.

"It is the land of the Osages."

"Indians?"

"Yes."

"Are they friendly?"

"Most often."

They rode on. And on. The sun burned their skin in the daytime and at night the bitter terrible cold ate into their bones like icy knives. Now they understood the need for all the extra blankets. There was no wood for cooking fires, nor for warmth, nor to ward off the wolves. The watchers stayed awake listening for the prowling feet of animals, expecting the sudden grip of teeth in their throats at every sound.

For a while there was no water except what they carried, for they had left the river now. They were beginning to hate this open land with nothing to rest the eye. They longed for the friendly rustle of leaves and the gentle shade of a tree, but they were determined men and kept their feelings to themselves. Hawk Eye seemed unmoved by the vastness. He rode on impassively, speaking only when spoken to. His impassiveness invoked confidence. His silence suggested he knew exactly where he was going. Beale hoped to God he did.

The monotony of the open land had a hypnotic effect on the riders. They kept their eyes fixed so far ahead that they were suddenly surprised to come over the top of a small hill and see in the hollow beneath a herd of buffalo grazing. Raising their shaggy, ugly heads, a couple of bulls gave the alarm and started galloping clumsily away.

"Buffalo, Buffalo!" the men shouted, galloping down among them. Immediately the air was filled with the thunder of hooves; dust rose, mingling with the steam and sweat of men and animals, all around them the press of great bodies striving to escape. Shots rang out, short tails and enormous heads moved frantically through the tumult. Beale took aim at a fat cow, hitting her in the deadly spot behind the shoulders. Down she went and a grizzled old bull turned on him with ferocity. Beale's horse leapt aside with such suddenness that Beale was almost thrown out of his saddle. The bull turned, its ugly head and fierce eyes almost touching him as the horse wrenched away. Lowering its head, the bull came at him a third time and Beale knew he was done for—there was no escape in the milling animals. Suddenly the bull jerked aside and sank down with a horrible lurch as Hawk Eye's lance entered its heart.

The herd rushed on, some of the men keeping up with it. Then, as suddenly as it began, the tumult was over and Beale and the others turned back to check the kill and start work on the animals.

Between them they had about 12 head of fine beasts. Setting up camp, they labored all day skinning and preparing the hides and cutting the best of the meat into broad sheets for drying. They hung it over cords of rawhide to dry in the sunshine. Now they had meat enough to last for a considerable time and skins that would fetch a good price.

Hawk Eye collected the dried dung of the buffalo and made fires over which they cooked some of the best meat. It tasted better than anything they had eaten for years.

Fortunately no one had been hurt by the reckless charge into the buffalo, but Hawk Eye told them they might not be so lucky another time.

There are two ways of hunting buffalo. One is approaching. This is the safer of the two, for the hunters quietly sneak up on the herd and shoot from a long or short range taking careful aim. The other is running, when the hunters overtake the herd on horseback, mingle among it and shoot the best beasts while riding at a gallop. This is the most exciting and highly dangerous hunting, because an exhausted, frantic beast will turn on the horse and rider, causing the horse to sidestep violently—a maneuver that can throw the rider under the hooves of the herd. Also it is difficult to take aim under these conditions: many a hunter has been killed or injured by a bullet from his own gun. This was the method that appealed to most hunters because of the excitement, and Beale and his company, while agreeing with Hawk Eye's cautions, had no intention of patiently stalking a herd.

They were to grow used to seeing the great herds of buffalo; sometimes as many as 100,000 moved across the plain. Ugly, shaggy, humped creatures, sometimes they were wild and skittish, other times curious and friendly. It was possible to walk up to a herd and even shoot one before the rest were alarmed and moved off.

Though some of the men considered them stupid, Hawk Eye said the buffalo were friends of the Indian and knew they only killed him for food when they were hungry, so he did not run away from them.

Beale came to share this view and, ugly though the beasts were, there was a kind of nobility about their ungainly movements as they traveled across the country, their size in keeping with its vastness.

Soon they were back at the river which, like the buffalo, they were to follow for many long days. Although Hawk Eye seemed to know where he was going, Beale and the men could see no landmarks that could guide them. True, there were stars at night, but they did not travel by night.

There were uneasy suspicions that Hawk Eye might be leading them to his Indian friends who would massacre them for their horses and supplies. Was this why he had insisted that Beale buy all those extra horses? It was well known that an Indian would do anything for a good horse and they had over 70 counting those carrying their baggage. These suspicions increased when Hawk Eye was seen sending signals across the plain from a hillock hidden from the camp by the baggage horses. Then there was the fact that although they had seen bands of Indians in the far distance, none had come anywhere near them. Was this because they knew they had only to wait and the company and horses would fall into their hands?

Beale did not want to listen to these suspicions. He trusted Hawk Eye and Monsieur Pierre, but when it was reported that the guide was continuing to signal to the Indians, he was concerned. Pierre had told him how the Indians of the plains communicate with each other by hand and arm gestures. Even though they speak a different language, they understand each other through this method. This system was extremely effective even over long distances. Beale was concerned because they were completely dependent on Hawk Eye to guide them through this empty wilderness. If he was a traitor there was no way of escape for them. The Indians could find them wherever they went in these open spaces. The small company was hopelessly outnumbered by the Indian bands. Beale determined they would not die without a fight. They'd make every shot a killer and Hawk Eye would be the first to go.

"I speak with you now?" It was Hawk Eye who had come up on him so quietly that Beale was startled.

"Yes, I'm glad to speak with you. I hear you have been signaling the Indians."

"Yes, I speak regular with my friends. I have good news for you from them."

"What do they say?"

"They say that if you give the best horse to chief as present, no trouble from Indian all way to Santa Fe."

Beale looked sharply at Hawk Eye. "How can this be true? There are many tribes."

"Yes, but this big chief. He tell others and you give only small presents to them."

Beale was doubtful. "Can we trust them or will they change their minds as soon as the chief gets the horse?"

"They are my friends, my brothers." Hawk Eye spoke with a pride that silenced Beale's doubts. Hawk Eye evidently trusted them completely; all Beale could do was hope such trust was well founded.

"When do we give them the horse? Does the chief choose or you?"

"It is not easy. We show chief how best is the horse. You race with him, you win."

"I race with the chief! Suppose he wins?"

"You must win race. For safety of journey is necessary. You have best horse, I know. It will be well. I tell chief you agree?"

"There is no other way?"

"No, it is hard to get this safety from chief, only because he my brother is it possible."

"Well, then I agree." But the more Beale thought about it, the more worried he became. He was a good rider but he had no experience in racing. How could he compete with an Indian who spent his life at it?

The men were of the same opinion. "Promise him a couple of horses, or even half a dozen, but don't get caught in that trap. No white man can outride a plains Indian. Their horses are incredible and they know every step of this land."

"It no good. Chief want race." Hawk Eye's face was impassive. "You race or all die," he said to Beale.

Later he came to Beale when he was alone. "There is no worry, you good rider and I bought horse no one can beat. Horse belong to Indian one time. You ride him every day, then race. I tell chief race in three days."

Beale was curious about the horse Hawk Eye thought so much of. All the horses were good but Beale had not noticed any one more outstanding than another.

42

"This is your horse," Hawk Eye said as he led a black mare over to Beale. "I take special care of her. She splendid horse." The mare nuzzled Hawk Eye; it was obvious that she knew him. He talked to her in some language Beale could not understand and the mare whinnied softly. She had the rounded muzzle of the Spanish Arab, a deep chest and powerful hindquarters. The muscles rippled under the shining black skin and there was no superfluous flesh on her anywhere.

"You ride her now?"

"Yes." Beale was impatient to mount and try her out.

"You ride Indian saddle, she like that."

"Well . . . all right."

"She know this land, she understand everything. You talk to her and she know you and what you want."

Beale found it was so; the mare was responsive and fast. There was a power in her that increased as she flew across the plain. Hawk Eye raced beside them and the mare easily outdistanced him. Beale began to feel some confidence. They'd give the chief a good race anyhow.

Hawk Eye, through the mysterious signalings, had decided upon the race course with the chief. The event would take place in the late afternoon.

The chief and a very large band of Indians could be seen approaching at dawn. Beale was curious to see for himself the differences between the Indians of the eastern seaboard and the plains Indian.

It was several hours before the two parties were close enough to see each other clearly and Hawk Eye said they should make camp and prepare for the afternoon as they were close to the race course now. Beale could not see that this land looked any different from all the rest but he agreed. The tents gave a welcome shade. All the men were keyed up

43

and Beale found it hard to keep calm. He knew he needed to keep all his wits about him. He was worried about several things: Would this be a fair race of one horse against another? Or was it a mere pretext to capture the whole lot? If by chance he should win would the chief keep his promise? If they lost what would become of them? Would they be tortured to death? Should they fight their way out or must they keep their shots for themselves?

Full of misgivings, Beale sought out Hawk Eye only to find him talking to the mare in a manner Beale would not have believed possible. The Indian was unlike his usual stoic self. There was an excitement about him that he tried to hide as soon as he saw Beale. His eyes sparkled in a manner Beale thought impossible in an Indian. Beale was about to speak when the drumming of hooves made them turn to see a band of Indians galloping directly into the camp at full tilt.

"None must move. No harm will come," Hawk Eye shouted before Beale could react.

"Stand fast," Beale shouted, "hold your fire." He ran ahead, Hawk Eye beside him, and stood waiting before the camp.

The Indians, lances held high, buffalo shields hanging on their backs, galloped with furious speed toward them. Suddenly, as if touched by an invisible hand, all lances were lifted and turned ready for attack. Beale felt the blood drumming in his ears with the thunder of the hoof beats. He felt as if the plain was shaking with the awful rhythm. This was the end then. What a fool he'd been to trust an Indian. It was too late for shooting now. The whole world was filled with galloping horses, shrieking Indians and whirling hooves. Hot breath and the steaming foam from bridles bit Beale's face as the band suddenly wheeled about two feet from him and roared past.

It was a magnificent performance of the most remarkable horsemanship. Beale and the whole company broke into cheers waving their hats in relief and admiration. By now the Indians were headed back to their own camp, lances upright. Beale turned to Hawk Eye.

"Is this the usual greeting?"

"They show you how they ride." Hawk Eye was noncommital.

"They ride very well. Their horses are fast."

"These are war horses. They have horse for buffalo, not so fast but very clever."

"Will they be visiting again before the race?"

"Maybe."

They did. They performed many feats of horsemanship in front of the camp. They rode at full gallop, each hanging over the side of his horse and shooting arrows under the horse's head so that they were protected by the horse's body against any bullet or arrow. They had absolute control and could act in unison without visible means of communication. Beale wondered how it was done.

"Have no fear, you and the mare will beat them," Hawk Eye said to Beale.

Beale found himself anxious to get the race over. The Indian show did not help his rather shaky belief in his racing ability. He was glad when Hawk Eye announced the time had come.

Hawk Eye went ahead to commune with the Indians and Beale followed with his men. A lance stood marking the starting post and another, far distant, marked the winning post. Beale was given no opportunity to go over the course but the terrain was the same as that they had been riding over for days.

As yet there was no sign of the chief. Hawk Eye came back and said Beale's men would take care of the start of the race, giving the starting signal, and the Indians would be at the finishing post.

"You mean we can't watch the finish?" one of the men

45

said incredulously. "We've got to see the finish," the men insisted, "why not divide up? Some of us at the finishing post and some here, the same with the Indians."

"No, it cannot be. You here. Indians there. You tell them, Captain Beale." Hawk Eye looked at Beale for confirmation.

"This is the best way?" Beale asked him.

"It is the way to win. You win this way."

"Very well. Let's do what he says, men. We don't have too much choice."

Then from the group of Indians came the chief. Befeathered and handsome he was an impressive sight mounted on a bay stallion. Beale could see that horse and rider belonged together, they would be a hard team to beat. The chief gave greetings which Beale returned and Beale felt the Indian look him over but, whatever he thought, he gave no sign. The chief seemed more interested in the horse than in Beale. He could hardly take his eyes off the mare.

They stood together at the starting post, the men silently standing around them.

Then they were off. The chief had the lead immediately, used as he was to a quick getaway. Beale was not worried. He had expected this. The mare took longer to get into her stride but she was a stayer.

They raced across the plain about two lengths apart. Beale kept urging the mare on, trying to lessen the gap. The mare was courageous and responded well. The gap grew shorter. Only one length now. Beale was low on her neck willing her to overtake the stallion but, try as she would, she could get no closer.

The chief never turned to look where they were; he was too sure of victory. They raced on and on without the mare gaining an inch, but she was still holding—the stallion was still one length ahead and no more. On and on they raced, oblivious to everything but the distant lance.

"Come on, old girl." Beale wished to God he knew the language Hawk Eye used to her.

The lance was getting closer; he could make out the Indians now. Beale was desperate and though he hated to do it, he dug his spurs into the mare's flanks. Startled, she leapt forward but Beale quickly realized he had made a mistake. He had upset her stride. The rhythm was momentarily broken and she dropped back.

"Good girl! . . ." Beale murmured encouragingly and then kept pouring every Indian word he knew into her ears. She was back in her stride and catching up, one length, half a length, now they were neck and neck racing for life. Life for himself and his men.

"Faster, faster." But the mare was giving all she had. She kept abreast, mane and tail streaming in the wind, her great hindquarters moving strongly. The Indian was worried now. Beale could see him urging the stallion on and the white showing in the beast's straining eyes as he moved ahead. The lance was less than a quarter of a mile away. To drop back would be the end, but the stallion was pulling ahead and the mare could give no more.

"We can't lose now," Beale thought desperately; but he could feel the mare falter, then, as if released by a spring she shot ahead, surprising Beale with her speed. Now the stallion was half a length behind, then one and a half, then they were past the post two lengths ahead.

The Indians surrounded them and Hawk Eye materialized, closely followed by Beale's men.

"I tell you she the best horse," Hawk Eye said, "now you give to chief."

They were never to forget this ceremony. The Indians admired courage and horsemanship above everything and the chief was so delighted with the mare that he gave many

47

gifts to Beale and promised protection across the whole land to Santa Fe.

That night Beale said to Hawk Eye, "I don't know what happened to the mare. All of a sudden she leapt forward as if she'd gotten a second wind. That's what won the race. She was beginning to falter up to then."

"She used to live with the horses of these Indians. She know them again and go to them. She mare of chief. She captured by other tribe and chief then get stallion for war horse. That why he so happy to get mare back. He never like stallion so much as mare and he thought never see her again."

Beale was incredulous. "You mean that you knew all this and planned it before we started?"

"There must be good plan to get to Santa Fe safe. This very good plan."

"But supposing the mare had been beaten by the stallion?"

"She would not, the chief know her when he saw her. He so glad to have her that not let stallion win. But mare so good she beat anyhow. Chief always your friend now."

Beale had no words to thank Hawk Eye. He and the men realized what the guide had done for them and how much foresight had gone into planning this journey. They were ashamed of their suspicions. From this time on, everything Hawk Eye said or did was accepted without question. They could not do enough for him.

The days passed by with monotonous similarity. They crossed the 98th meridian which marked east from west, making good progress until one of the men surprised a rattler and was badly bitten in the leg just above the riding boot. Joe used his medical knowledge as best he could and Beale helped him with all the remedies he knew, but they were all aware that there wasn't much to be done for a rattler bite.

They made no protest when Hawk Eye brought some evil-looking mess of herbs which he rubbed on the hideous, swollen limb. What harm could anything do? The poor sufferer was barely conscious, his breath coming in painful gasps, but he swallowed the stuff Hawk Eye gave him, fully knowing that he would die anyway. The men hung around in little groups waiting for the end which they hoped would not be long. Why prolong the poor fellow's agony? They did not sleep much that night. They had become a closely knit group after all these days in the saddle together. It was hard to lose a man and a good one too. Every so often one or two would make their way to the tent to see if there was anything to be done, or just to sit and share the watch with Joe and Beale and Hawk Eye. They'd stay a while and then their place would be taken by others.

Toward dawn, Beale thought the man was breathing easier. "He seems easier, Joe, look, his breath's real easy now."

"It's a sign of the end, Tom. They always seems better before they go."

They looked at each other remembering the times they'd shared with this man. He'd been a good friend and comrade and he deserved something better than a lonely grave in this desert. He had a wife and family too.

Beale went out of the tent to look at the fading stars. The air was chill as it always was at night. How flimsy was life, he thought. This time yesterday morning this man was getting ready to ride, full of life and expecting to go on for another 40 years. Saddened, he went back to stand beside Joe. "What is it?" he asked, seeing Joe and Hawk Eye bending over the man.

"He seems better. I can't believe it! Get some liquid into

him. Any of that gravy left over from last night's stew meat?
Water, anything."

The men ran to get what they could. The fires were
quickly going and everyone had a suggestion for strength-
giving nourishment. They were pathetically eager to do
something. None wanted to die in this place and lie forever
alone. Each identified with the sufferer in his own way. Only
Hawk Eye was not surprised.

"Indian medicine very good. I know he get well."

By noon there was a definite improvement and they
dared to hope for recovery. "Damndest thing I ever saw,"
Joe said. "Never would have believed it if I hadn't seen it
with my own eyes. He must be pretty tough to stand up to a
rattler bite."

"Do you think it was the Indian medicine?" Beale
asked.

"God knows, but something worked. And I can tell you
I'm going to try my damndest to get some of that Indian
medicine from Hawk Eye. Never know when we might want
it."

They were delayed almost three weeks before the man
was fit to ride again, but by the time they reached Santa Fe
he was as good as new.

The worst part of the journey started when they left the
Arkansas river to cross the Cimarron desert. This is a stretch
of the worst land in the area. No trees, no grass, no water.
The sand was burning by day and bitterly cold by night. A
harsh wind blew sand into everything and despite all the precautions they took the horses suffered, and several of the
men were sick so that they had to travel slowly. Even Hawk
Eye seemed to shrink and wrinkle more and more as the days
went by. Not being used to mirages, the men would waste
energy galloping toward shallow streams and even rivers that
appeared on the horizon, in spite of Hawk Eye's warnings.

The strange shapes of the sand dunes and rocks made them feel as if they were riding through a nightmare. It was an awful test of endurance. Only men strong in body and soul could get through unharmed. Only the fact that they were three-quarters of the way to Santa Fe helped them hang on.

"Soon we will see grass and water, then trees and mountains," Hawk Eye said one day when things were at their worst and water very carefully rationed.

"How many more days?" Beale asked.

"Three, maybe."

There was silence, each man wondering if he could last another day. Then after two more days they saw a bush and some coarse grass in the distance.

"Look!" exclaimed Beale, "grass!"

Lackluster eyes turned toward where he was pointing but no one increased his pace—another mirage?

"We are over the worst; by night there will be water," Hawk Eye said.

Beale could have wept. "Thank God," he said quietly, looking at the exhausted men and equally exhausted animals. Though they still had many miles to go, it was through land hospitable to men.

5.

They reached Santa Fe on December 1 and made camp about ten miles from the city. They didn't want to risk being seized and thrown in prison so they considered it wiser to camp outside. Beale and a couple of the men would ride in with Hawk Eye to see how the land lay and to test the temper of the people.

It was late in the afternoon before Beale and the others set out for Santa Fe, riding at an easy pace so as not to attract too much attention. It was a cold, bitter day but they didn't notice the weather in their satisfaction over being at last in this rich city whose fame was known to all who traveled this way. St. Louis was nothing compared to this. Santa Fe seemed fabulous and exotic, different from anything Beale had known or imagined. He wasn't prepared for the size and beauty of the buildings. Santa Fe was old long before Williamsburg or Richmond was founded.

In spite of the cold there were many people in the streets, but no one paid much attention to Beale and his party, although an occasional glance was thrown their way. Reassured by the lack of interest they created, they rode on into the Plaza which, as in all Spanish cities, was situated in the center of the community.

The Governor's Palace, with the date 1610 marked on it, faced on the Plaza. It was in the dungeons of this Palace that

Zebulon Pike had been incarcerated when captured in 1807 while exploring the Rio Grande del Norte. In fact at the very moment that Beale rode into the Plaza, two Americans, Auguste Choteau and Joseph de Mun, suspected of aiding a Mexican uprising against the Spanish, were languishing in the dark horror of this prison.

Riding down one of the streets off the Plaza, Beale saw the sign of a *pulperia*, the Spanish word for tavern, which looked cheerful and clean.

"Let's try this place," Beale said, "we might find out how things are regarding travelers here. At any rate we can try their vittles. What do you say, Hawk Eye?"

"I say try it."

They dismounted and tied their horses to the hitching post outside. A few Indians wrapped in blankets leaned against the wall, fixing them with a disinterested stare.

Do you think it's safe to leave the horses unguarded?"

"If we expect civility they're likely to show it. If they want to steal the horses they'll take them whether they're guarded or not."

They pushed open the heavy carved door and stepped into the tavern. A large, cheerful looking fire, winking off the bottles standing on the bar and on the little tables, was blazing in the enormous open hearth. There was a good smell of cooking food and they suddenly realized how hungry they were for food cooked in an oven and served at a table. As they sat down, a dark, handsome woman came over to them.

"Buenas dias, señores."

Hawk Eye had only a smattering of the language but answered, "Gracias, señora, deseamos muchos carnes y vino."

Wine was quickly supplied and platters of chili and beans followed without much delay. It was good and the men fell on it like wolves. This pleased the beauteous señora who, they later found out, was the owner and watched over most of the cooking herself.

"You like my food, no?" she asked in Spanish.

"Si, si, muy rico," Hawk Eye replied for them.

Beale understood enough Spanish to follow the conversation and he became uneasy when the señora began asking who they were and where they came from and why they were in the city. He didn't relish being set upon by the Indians outside the door.

"Tell the señora that we are hunting buffalo and bear and we have camped near here so that we can rest our horses and stock up with provisions. We shall move on when the weather is better."

The lady's face was very expressive and Beale could see her assessing them with her sharp, dark eyes. He wondered if she were a spy for the governor. Spanish prisons were notoriously unhealthy and Beale had no desire to see the inside of one.

"Ask her if visitors are welcome to Santa Fe."

The señora looked offended by the question. Hawk Eye hastened to translate.

"She says of course travelers are welcome. This is a very hospitable city. Only those who come to steal trade or other things from us are unwelcome."

"Tell her that we come to buy with good money or we will exchange with goods we brought from the East."

They carefully avoided the word "trader," stressing that they were hunters and only wanted enough to satisfy their own personal needs. The señora seemed satisfied and said that all the party were welcome at her inn and if they by chance had a clock or a watch she would be overjoyed to buy it from them, as her clock, a family heirloom, was now beyond repair.

Clocks and watches were scarce everywhere, but in Santa Fe they had enormous value as did any manufactured goods, because they were practically unobtainable.

Beale knew that the señora would be a good friend to have. She could do much for their comfort during the winter. The place was comfortable and well run, the few customers seemed respectable enough, and the food and wine were excellent.

"Tell the señora that I will find out if any from my party can spare his watch for her. As we are hunters, not traders, we only have our personal property and a few goods for Indian presents.

The señora's eyes sparkled as Hawk Eye translated to her.

"When will you bring it, she wants to know."

"I'm not sure. Possibly tomorrow."

To their immense relief the horses were waiting when they went outside. But what they did not notice was that there was one less Indian than when they went in. It was getting dark now so they mounted quickly and were on their way.

Once clear of the city they quickened their pace, but they had gone hardly more than two or three hundred yards when they heard hoof beats behind them. In a moment they were surrounded by uniformed riders formidably armed. One who was evidently the officer in charge said in English, "My orders are to ask you to accompany me back to the city, señor. It will be well to come willingly." He was polite, but Beale detected the steel in his voice.

"We have already enjoyed a visit to your city. We do not want to return at this time unless there is some special reason."

"You have no choice, señor. The Governor desires to have you interrogated. We have had much difficulty with

56

gringos lately."

There was no possibility of escape without endangering the rest of the company, so Beale said, "We will go with you as we have no choice, but we are peaceful travelers. We are hunters of bear and buffalo and cause no trouble to anyone. In fact, we need to buy provisions so we bring money to the city."

"You can explain all this when we reach the city, señor. Please hand over your arms."

There was nothing to do but obey, though each man resented bitterly handing over his gun to these men without firing a shot. Beale could feel their resentment, but he knew it was better for them to be seized than to risk the lives of the 28 remaining at the camp. It was possible that they were safe enough out there.

They rode into the city in silence. It was almost completely dark by now, but the Plaza was lit by huge torchlights which made it look even more foreign and exotic. They were told to dismount at the Governor's Palace and then led through a side door into a paneled room which appeared to be a hearing chamber of some kind. Beale was relieved at this. He had feared that they would be thrown into the dungeons without interrogation and left there to rot, forgotten by everyone.

A man in a uniform similar to the horseman's but more ornate, came in and sat on a throne-like chair of carved wood which was on a raised dais.

Beale could see Hawk Eye casting his eyes around as if wondering how to escape. Surely the Governor was not interested in an Indian guide—but he didn't have much time to wonder—he was told to step forward and answer the questions of Don Aribear.

"Why have you come to this city?"

"We are hunters and we have traveled a very long distance to hunt buffalo and bear on these plains. Because it is

57

winter and we cannot hunt, we decided to camp near the city in order to rest and buy provisions for the hunting trips we'll make as soon as the weather allows it. If we are not welcome, señor, we can move on since we have only just arrived and not settled yet."

"From where did you come?"

"St. Louis."

"Before that?"

"Big Lick."

"Big Lick? Where is that place?"

"It is a small settlement in Virginia, close to where I was born."

"Why did you come to hunt here? Why not hunt in the northern plains?"

"We heard that the buffalo are larger and the skins better in this part of the world. And this city is famous and we wanted to see it."

"Are you expecting to trade?"

"Only for provisions necessary for hunting."

Then Beale was told to stand back and Hawk Eye was brought forward and asked similar questions. He said little other than he was employed by Beale to guide his party from St. Louis to Santa Fe where they told him they wanted to hunt buffalo and bear.

"How many are there in the party?"

"Thirty men," Hawk Eye replied.

"Where are the rest?" Don Aribear said to Beale.

"They are with the horses making camp for the night outside the city."

"They expect to trade, do they not?" He looked sharply at Beale.

"No, señor, we are a party of hunters all seeking buffalo and bear. None has any goods to trade. We have only a few Indian presents apart from our personal needs."

58

"We will soon know if you speak the truth. The camp is being searched."

Beale was alarmed. He hoped the men would take the search calmly and not start any shooting.

"You look troubled, señor. If you have no trading goods and are but peaceful hunters, you have nothing to fear."

"We have experienced much danger, señor. These are not easy times. My men may not understand the reason for the search and refuse to allow it. You will not hold this against them?"

"We will see, señor. I cannot answer for my men if yours start fighting. But let us suppose that you are what you say and we allow you to spend the winter here. What are your plans?"

"We would like to buy provisions and procure a guide for our hunting trip. Hawk Eye only contracted to come this far and he hopes to get another party who want to go to St. Louis. Then we would hope to enjoy the taverns and places of entertainment in the city. We have had a long, hard journey and we will appreciate the comforts of good food and wine and pleasant company."

Don Aribear smiled for the first time. "We will see." He turned to the officer who had brought them in. "Take these men to their camp and then you know what to do."

These words did nothing to remove their apprehension. Beale was fearful of what might have happened at the camp and regretted that he had come to the city. They mounted quickly and rode blindly along with their escort. Soon they were able to see the campfires burning but all seemed very quiet. When they rode up, Beale could see a number of uniformed men going through the baggage, closely watched by the company. The search was soon completed, the only articles in doubt being the Indian presents.

"Can you explain these, señor?"

59

"They are gifts for the Indians. We pass through territory where the Indians are hostile and we have to buy their goodwill with these gifts. As you know, señor, it is the usual custom."

"You have made a long journey simply to hunt buffalo."

"Yes, we have traveled a long way and endured much hardship to hunt here where we are told we can find the best buffalo and the best bear in the land. You could not prevent us from this hunting after all we suffered to get here."

The officers in charge then went apart and conferred together. Beale looked around at the men. Some were looking to him as if waiting for a signal to set upon the soldiers, but Beale shook his head. Then the officer who had brought Beale back said, "We are happy to find that you are but simple hunters, señor, and we welcome you to Santa Fe. Call upon me at any time if I can give you assistance." Calling his men he ordered them to return the guns. Then he made a polite gesture and was gone.

This encounter, which caused much resentment among the company, turned out to be of great help to Beale in the future. Once established as hunters, Beale and his men were not troubled by the city officials and from this meeting with the captain of the guard, a man named Gomez, Beale made friendships among the people which made their winter stay much more comfortable and fruitful.

Beale wondered if it was the señora from the pulperia who had reported them, and the next time he saw her he tried delicately to find out. But the señora gave nothing away. In fact she treated them so well that Beale decided that even if she had reported them it had turned out for the best and he would not hold it against her.

The Spanish were suspicious of American travelers; they feared these visitors were sent to spy out the land with a view to taking the territory by one means or another. Santa Fe was under the Spanish flag but there was a very strong Mexican Indian majority who were restless under Spanish rule. They had revolted once and the Spanish feared that they might go over to any other power who came to liberate them. The French were a threat to Spain as were the British but it was the Americans they feared most of all. For this reason they did not want to encourage trading with the Americans as this would bring in more foreigners and make ties with outside powers. Trade conquers more surely than arms, so it was not until the Mexicans were in control again in 1821 that American trade was welcomed.

With the help of some of the Indians, Beale and his men built some cabins for the winter. They thought it better to remain encamped than risk arrest if the people should turn against them. They went into the city regularly and patronized most of the pulperias and places of entertainment.

Beale wanted to find a good guide for the buffalo hunting and so he sought the help of the señora and of the captain of the guards. Both recommended a man, half Mexican, a little bit French and a smaller bit Spanish. His name was Carlos Sanchez but Beale's men called him Charlie. Charlie was no longer young but he was wiry and tough. He knew the area and the buffalo as well as grizzlies and the various Indian tribes. He could speak many of their languages and had a good-humored disposition.

Hawk Eye had contracted to come only as far as Santa Fe because he knew little of the area beyond. He very quickly fell in with a group of men who wanted to make their way to St. Louis. He was glad to go: he feared Santa Fe and mistrusted the people around it. Although he had not told Beale, Hawk Eye's brother had been in Santa Fe when the two Americans were seized and put in the dungeons. Hawk Eye decided he was safer at St. Louis. When they were taken for interrogation, Hawk Eye thought he was as good as dead; he never expected to come out of the Palace alive. He was so grateful that he wanted to put as much distance as he could between himself and the city in case the Great Spirit changed his mind.

The dreary months of winter were brightened by displays of dancing by the Indians and Mexicans, and by a couple of Indian magicians. It was at the Pulperia Conchita that they first saw the magician. He was a tall, majestic looking individual with the kind of dark penetrating eyes that could hypnotize a person. Whether it was the dim, wine-soaked atmosphere of the place or whether the magic was really as big as the people believed, Beale never found out, but things went on which raised the hair on their heads and turned their blood cold.

The magician worked with one helper and when they were not performing, they kept out of sight so that they were more sought after when they did appear. No one quite knew where they originated; they appeared every winter and might stay a week or the whole season. It depended on how they felt or, as Charlie said, "how the spirit moved them."

The night Beale saw them perform for the first time, he sat transfixed. The magician had ordered the room arranged so that the little tables were in a semi-circle, and he and his helper had their backs to the open hearth.

The flames leaping and crashing as a log fell and the smoke swirling behind them made the whole thing appear like a scene from the devil's kitchen. First, the magician drew the leather belt from around his helper's waist and it dropped to the ground as an enormous snake with fangs dripping poison and tail rattling. Then amidst the horror and confusion of all, he calmly took it by the tail and wrapped it back around the boy's waist, the head with its

62

forked tongue darting hither and thither until it lapsed into a buckle.

The boy handed the magician a bowl filled with broken arrowheads which the magician took out one at a time with a tremendous flourish. He put it in his mouth with a hideous grimace, swallowed it and reached for another. After swallowing ten, he went into dreadful convulsions and finally coughed them all up as five whole arrowheads. The helper then carried the bowl around for inspection. Another night the helper thrust a great spear through the body of the magician and pulled it out of his back. Blood flowed onto the floor and then stopped abruptly and the magician was seen to be absolutely unscarred.

After each performance the magician would call for volunteers to try out any of the feats of magic, but there were never any takers. When the wind was screaming outside and the wolves howling in the distance the magician seemed the incarnation of terror and supernatural power. Beale found himself believing against his will. He had never understood how a man could be influenced by magic until this time, and he realized that such a man as this could have a tremendous effect on the minds of the watchers. He would be a valuable ally if he could be used by a leader.

Women were easy to obtain. There were several well-run bagnios where a man might spend a pleasurable night with an understanding girl. Beale rarely visited them because he found a friend in Señora Conchita s daughter and they made him very comfortable in their rooms above the pulperia.

But he was kept busy finding out all he could about the area and about the buffalo and bear. People were glad to talk in the long, dark days and the even longer nights. There was too much drinking and too many quarrels for Beale's liking. He knew how hard this was on the morale of active men.

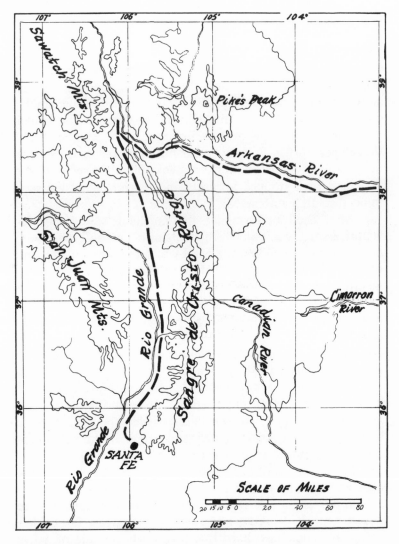

From Santa Fe to the gold find

6.

The winter proved long and hard and, in spite of the divertissements provided, all the men were impatient to be in the saddle again. Beale himself was restless and irritable from the confinement but like the others he knew there was nothing to do but wait for spring. The snow fell with a quiet persistence most of the time. Other times it was carried by a howling, biting wind which tore the skin with red hot lashes.

Santa Fe had its share of bagnios and Beale and his men patronized them pretty well during their stay; also the dark rooms of taverns where it was possible to gamble away the proceeds of a year's work in an evening. There was an element of danger to the patrons since the Governor frowned on all this and soldiers would raid every now and again and indiscriminately haul off a few patrons, taking all the available cash and valuables at the same time. This risk did not discourage Beale or any of his company; rather it made the places more interesting to them. All the same they were so restless by the end of February that it was agreed that a small party of three or four would make a short hunting trip as soon as the weather cleared a bit.

They had all been out shooting fresh meat from time to time, but this was mostly small stuff as the snow had made it impossible to travel far. A longer trip might get a buffalo and in any case it would take some of the meanness out of man and horse.

In every pulperia, in fact wherever men gathered, a tale was told of a remarkable herd of buffalo north of Santa Fe. These buffalo were larger and more powerful than any others. The skins were worth double the price of an ordinary buffalo and among this herd were several pure white animals, the prize skins that the Indians and most traders would give any price for.

Few had ever seen this herd and no one had actually shot one himself but several men swore they had seen a skin and described it as being magnificent; bigger, softer and heavier than any other. As soon as the weather permitted, Beale and his men were going after this herd.

It was about the third week in March when the weather improved enough for a party to set out. Nine men started on a northeast course seeking the mysterious herd, intending to be gone not more than three or four days.

Charlie, who claimed he knew where the herd traveled, went along with them. The air felt sharp and good. Riding across the open land they felt new life surge into them. The sun warmed their flesh and the miseries of their cramped winter existence sloughed off like a snakeskin.

They had been riding for about three hours when they sighted black spots on the horizon. "Buffalo," shouted Charlie, and without exchanging a word, every man put his horse to a gallop. Was it the mysterious herd?

The ground was hard and dangerously pitted with the holes of small animals. Here and there patches had thawed to a sogginess into which a horse could sink suddenly and throw his rider. But they didn't care; they rode on recklessly, forgetting everything but the excitement of the chase. Stopping for neither food nor rest they galloped on, determined to overtake the herd. By late afternoon they were close enough to see that these were gigantic animals, far larger than any they had ever seen. The tale was true! Now they were more eager than ever. Urging their horses on they sped, ignoring every risk, but the fading light forced them to halt and make camp for the night. They knew it was impossible to shoot in this light even if they overtook the herd.

Ravenous from their long ride, the men soon got fires going and feasted off the provisions they had brought with them.

"Fresh buffalo meat tomorrow night," someone shouted and the men answered with a cheer.

It was cold sleeping under the stars again. Great mountains to their left gave some protection from the chill wind that came off the snows. The sound of melting ice and snow crashing down, and the rushing of the swollen streams kept them awake for a while. Watches were set and the fires kept going through the night, not only for warmth but to keep off the wolves and other unwanted visitors.

Soon after daybreak they were off in the direction they had last seen the buffalo. For several hours they rode on without a glimpse of them, then suddenly the beasts appeared on the horizon. A magnificent sight. The Indians used only the skins of the cows so there were usually more bulls than cows in the herd, but this herd had plenty of fat cows and calves, probably because they were wary enough to keep out of the reach of men.

Unlike some herds these buffalo were wild and timid and kept on the move. It seemed as if they knew they were being followed and kept themselves slightly ahead; not very far but well out of range of the guns. It was as if the buffalo were playing a game with them.

"They're not acting like buffalo," one man complained. "Are you sure they're buffalo, Charlie?"

"Si, señor, but Indians say they are spirits of great chiefs and cannot be killed."

They were certainly acting strangely. Buffalo are strange animals: Sometimes they appear so stupid that they allow a man to walk up to them and even shoot one of them before the rest will realize the danger and get away. Other times

67

they are so wary that it takes tremendous skill and knowledge of their habits to get near them. Usually a rider can overtake them as they stop to feed and drink, but this herd was alert and always ahead.

When the men set out they felt sure of getting some of the great buffalo. They had agreed they would stop for nothing but this special herd, so they rode on and on, disregarding all else, keeping their eyes fixed on the great plain ahead. They even forgot the Indians and the possibility of attack. Once a great bear coming out of hibernation stood up to gaze at them but they ignored him, scarcely aware of his presence.

Three days passed, then four, then five and still they were riding without overtaking them. The buffalo would appear on the horizon, then vanish. It was like chasing a mirage except the men knew they were real.

On the eighth night they were preparing their few remaining rations when one of the men noticed something glittering in the crevice of the rocks. He knew something about metal and this looked as if it might be gold. They were likely looking rocks; they could have veins of gold or silver. He poked around with his knife and got out a piece of ore that most surely contained gold. Unable to control his excitement, he shouted, "There's gold here! These rocks are full of it!"

For a moment there was silence; they every man left what he was doing to rush over and look for himself. Gold it was indeed, and plenty of it.

Forgetting even the buffalo, the men began to attack the ground with their bare hands, stones, anything that came to hand. Gold! Who cared for buffalo when there was gold?

Back at Santa Fe, Beale was worried. What had become of the hunting party? They were to have been back in three or four days. Almost three weeks had gone by with no sign of them. "If they're not back by nightfall, we'd best send a party out to search for them," he said.

A search party of six men was ordered to make preparations to leave the following day. The weather was reasonably good but it was hard to tell what it was like farther north. Maybe the hunting party had been lost in a storm or had fallen in with hostile Indians. There was good reason for alarm.

Everything had gone well with the stocking of the wagons and the purchase of provisions and ammunition. Beale was ready to venture out on their first hunting trip after the winter, but he was unwilling to move unless he knew what had become of the hunters. The loss of ten men was bad; thirty was the minimum for safety in a land where their lives could be at stake daily.

It was about three in the afternoon when two men from the hunting party were seen riding toward the camp. Beale set out to meet them, anxious to know what had happened to the rest.

The men were tired and hungry but full of news. As soon as they were near enough they shouted, "All's well—we're rich!"

Later they told the whole story. "All must come and bring our belongings and gear. There's enough there to keep us digging for years. We'll need enough provisions to last a good while. You won't believe what you see. It's the richest strike you've ever dreamed about. We'll all be rich."

Cautioning the men to say nothing about the gold outside the camp, Beale went about the business of completing his preparations, adding tools and other equipment to the total. They gave out that the hunting party had sighted the gigantic herd of buffalo and they were all going to join the hunt. Señora Conchita tried to dissuade him, but Beale said, "We intend to bring back some of those hides to prove what great hunters we are."

"But, mi amigo, no one has ever killed one of those buffalo. They are not of reality. They are of the imagination only."

"Two of my men came back to get us. One has seen them close. He says they are magnificent. There are several white ones also. We will be rich, senora, rich!"

The señora shook her head. She had grown fond of Beale and his men. In fact she would have accepted any one of them into her home and bed. She hated to see them go chasing a chimera like this.

"Stay with me, señor. Let your men go and bring the buffalo back to you. It is necessary for you to stay and keep up your friendships here."

Beale smiled at her. "You are too kind to us. Part of me would like to stay with a lady as lovely as you, but you know how it is with a man. He must be off riding and hunting if he is to be happy. I must go after the buffalo and see for myself if they are as wonderful as they say."

"Hasta la vista, then. It is useless to try to turn your mind when you have set it one way, but I will miss you, señor."

The talk among the men was of nothing but the gold. They surrounded the two asking for every detail. No one slept. Each lay dreaming of riches and what it meant to his future.

Because of the wagons they made slower progress than the others had made and it was about twelve days before they reached the little camp the men had set up. The first thing Beale did was to examine the gold. Was it really gold, or some similar metal? The ore was rich, probably richer than most. It was strange looking, different from much that Beale had seen. But he recognized it as the rich sylvanite ore that contains both gold and silver. This ore is brittle and varied in color from a brassy yellow to almost white.

The men had gotten out a good deal of the stuff already.

Each had his own stashed in a saddlebag or some cooking utensil. Beale saw that some order must be made regarding the gold or trouble could start and ruin them all. After the horses were attended to and the meal eaten, Beale called the men together. It was hard to get them away from the vein, but eventually they came.

Speaking in no uncertain terms, Beale told them that this was most surely gold with silver mixed in the ore. "It's as rich a vein as we could hope for, but unless we get the digging under control it's not going to do us much good." Beale reminded them how far they were from any human habitation and that no amount of gold could buy horses and provisions in this place. Therefore they must reach agreement and set some rules.

"I suggest that we agree to work in shifts and share all that we get out equally among us. No one could get out of here alone so it's to our advantage to stick together. Anyone causing trouble will be given a horse and enough provisions to get him to Santa Fe; then he's on his own. Beale said if the men agreed he would draw up a paper and all could sign it in turn. So it was agreed and the paper signed, then shifts were set so that the horses were taken care of and food cooked by all in turn.

By common consent all thought of hunting was set aside. The men worked under the blazing sun and through the pelting rain. Nothing stopped them and it seemed the gold was inexhaustible.

When the first excitement was over, the men settled down to regular shifts of digging gold, hunting, exercising the horses or preparing food. And the hoard of gold grew and grew. Sometimes Beale would look at it, mesmerized by its magic. Gold, the metal that ruled all things! Gold, that bought men's souls and bodies! Gold, the king of the world!

The area around Buford's - about 1819

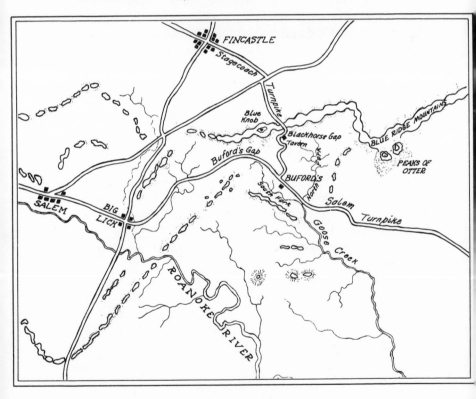

7.

The Beale party had been working for over a year when they began to talk of home and what they should do about the gold. There was always the danger that someone might stumble on their secret and betray them. Also the Indians could fall upon them at any time and massacre them if they came in any large numbers. If the gold were carried back to Virginia at least wives and relatives could enjoy it should anything happen to the men.

That night they discussed the situation around the fire. Some were for striking camp, sharing out what they had and making for home. Others were in favor of cleaning out the vein. They might never get back to this place and the loss of a year wasn't much compared with what it was worth in gold.

Finally it was agreed that Beale should go back with a few of the men, take part of the gold and silver, and hide it in a cave near Buford's Tavern which all the men knew about. The rest of the company would stay and keep working on the vein. They would wait a year and if Beale didn't return they would send another party back with gold. That is, if the gold was holding out. If not, they would strike camp and all make their way back to Big Lick with the gold and silver.

Ten hundred and fourteen pounds of gold and thirty-eight hundred and twelve pounds of silver were securely stowed in iron cooking pots and covered with iron lids. In order to take suspicion from the treasure, hides of buffalo and bear and other animals were piled over them in the wagons. The journey back was extremely hazardous and for the first 500 miles the whole company escorted Beale, and then he went on with ten of the men. Before parting, however, it was agreed that Beale would choose some honest person in the Lynchburg-Big Lick area who, if the company were in favor of him, should be entrusted with the secret of the whereabouts of the treasure. It was considered necessary to have someone other than themselves in on the secret so that if anything happened to Beale and the company, this person would carry out their wishes.

Beale hoped that the Indian chief would honor the promise of protection given almost two years earlier, but with the whole company going along the first 500 miles, this would see him through the most dangerous part of the journey. While the men were away, Charlie would supervise the Indians who had been working for them for over a year.

They took a southeasterly course until they hit the Arkansas river again. Going was slow with the loaded wagons but they offered protection against the weather and attack, so although the journey was much more tedious it was easier than the first time. Whether the chief kept his promise or whether the wagons and the number of men offered protection, they suffered no attack from Indians. Even when Beale and the ten men who were going with him parted from the rest of the company, they were not harassed by Indians.

Although Beale would have liked to stop in St. Louis and renew acquaintance with Monsieur Pierre and Hawk Eye, he decided not to do this, but rather to send in two men to get more provisions and move on quickly. He did not want to risk the chance of the wagons being searched. They could renew acquaintances on the way back.

After leaving St. Louis they came into more familiar landscape and both men and horses began to pick up speed, but still they had to stop and cut a way for the wagons from time to time. After the dry dusty plains it was a tremendous relief to be back where the air was moist and clean. They wondered about Nellie and her husband, whether he had come back and rebuilt their home or whether he was dead. Again they resisted the desire to stop and renew acquaintance.

It was late November before they sighted Big Lick. Once through Buford's Gap they rested before going further.

"We could make Buford's Tavern before night," said Beale, "it might be better to do that than to stay in Big Lick. The fewer places we stop, the fewer chances of being searched or asked questions."

"Do you think we should risk staying at Buford? There'll be plenty of folks there and they're bound to be nosing around finding out what's going on."

"It would look more natural to go there. It's what we would do if we had nothing more than skins in the wagons. If we start skulking around they're sure to think we've got something to hide," Beale replied.

"He's right. I vote we push on to Buford and act like we've come back with skins to sell in Richmond or somewheres and the hunting's so good the others have stayed out west and we're going back to join 'em."

So it was agreed; they planned to stay at Buford until the gold and silver was hidden and then disperse to their homes or friends until Beale was ready to make the return journey. Although they could have used a couple of days' rest, they could not relax for a moment with the stuff still in the wagons.

Silas, the same Negro who had looked after Beale's

75

horse many times before, came around to meet them. His face broke into a smile when he saw Beale. "Well, suh, Cap'n Beale, you back from that West? Sure good to see you. Wagons too! You sure done plenty huntin', you rich man now."

"Sure glad to see you, Silas," Beale said. "We did pretty well out there. We ought to get a good price for these skins. They're valuable so you watch no one goes near them."

"I sure will, Cap'n Beale, I sure will." The Negro flashed his ready smile and called for some others to help him with the horses. Beale felt a load off his shoulders. They had been wondering how to safeguard the wagons. Skins were valuable but not so valuable that men would guard them night and day. It would look suspicious if they were too anxious, yet Beale did not want anyone poking around looking at the skins, lest they come upon the gold. A strange servant might have been tempted to do this but Silas was attached to Beale who had always treated him well, and Beale knew that he could trust him to watch over the wagons without any fear that he would tamper with them.

"The sooner we get that stuff out of there the better," one of the men muttered to Beale. "I can't think of anything but what's in those wagons."

"You're right. First thing in the morning we'll go look over the cave and then we can figure out the best way to get the stuff up there."

Fortunately there were not many people in the tavern. It wasn't stagecoach night and it was too late for most people. So giving the excuse that they were exhausted from the journey they had a quick meal and settled down for the night. Two men slept in each wagon, ostensibly to save the cost of lodging, and Beale and the rest shared two rooms upstairs.

The feel of good featherbeds and soft pillows was not

enough to make them sleep well: the gold and silver was too heavy on their minds. As soon as it was light, Beale and five men started up the old road from Buford's leaving the other five to keep an eye on things.

Even though it was cold and the ground hard from frost, it was good to be back on familiar ground. The landscape seemed friendly. To their right, the Peaks of Otter loomed benevolently. Through the leafless trees they could see the hills and valleys they knew so well and they amused themselves picking out the old landmarks. It didn't take them long to get to the cave. They could ride most of the way but had to dismount and climb over boulders to enter.

"I'll sure be glad to get the stuff in there."

"We all will," answered Beale, stooping and making his way through the low opening.

"Take care there's no bear," one of the men warned, "they use these caves in winter."

Beale stepped inside gingerly feeling his way. His foot struck something soft and spongy—a bear! "Where's that lantern, quick!"

"Here, I'm lighting it."

A flame flickered up through the dark cave, and Beale saw, not a bear but a heap of hay and straw and leaves stretching back into the depths of the cave. He bent down and pushed the stuff aside with his boot. Underneath were sacks of potatoes and other root vegetables.

"Potatoes!" he exclaimed, "the farmers must be storing their crops in here."

"God, it's a good thing we didn't get here earlier in the year. Now what do we do:" the man with the lantern said.

"We'll have to figure out something else. The ground's too hard for digging. What about that cave over the other side of the mountain?"

"You mean that bear den?"

"Yes, the one where we shot that bear a few years ago. No one knows about that."

"How could we get the stuff up there? It's pretty hard going and those pots are heavy."

"You're right, we'd have to do it on foot and handling those pots in that place would be nearly impossible."

Outside in the cold wind they discussed what they should do. They could wait for a mild spell and bury it, or they could decide on another cave or bear den, put the treasure in and block it with stones and boulders.

Finally it was this latter method they decided on. No one wanted to keep the gold around any longer than was necessary. It had been hanging around their necks for so long that they couldn't wait to free themselves from the anxiety.

"I vote we go look over this other place and then get the stuff and finish the job today."

"Better not be in too much of a hurry," Beale warned, "we've got to figure a way to carry it and get it out without being seen."

"What about a sled?"

"No good over rocks."

"We could get a wagon part way."

"Yes, but what'll it look like taking a wagon there? They'll know we're up to something right away."

"It's best to move it by hand," Beale said, "it's the only way to keep it quiet."

"But how? It's mighty heavy."

"Figure something."

Back at the tavern they had a good meal of ham and eggs and talked things over with the other five men. All were of one mind: get the job done. It was agreed that they would get as close to the place as they could under cover of darkness, carrying the pots with them. As soon as it was light they would put the treasure in and secure the place.

They got together secretly five stout pieces of timber and some strong chains. One pot was to be hung by its handle over each piece of timber and two men would carry it, one at each end. They could go abreast where the way was wide enough and one behind the other where the going was difficult. They would be paced a distance apart so if one pair was discovered the others could hide.

Only Beale and one other man slept in the tavern that night. The others slept in the wagons, though they pretended they were going to sleep upstairs. They waited their chance to duck out unseen and stayed in the wagons. Beale and the other man made the beds appear slept in but they could not sleep and two hours before dawn they were out with the wagons getting the shaded lanterns ready and helping each pair off.

Beale went ahead of them all to lead the way and to make sure there was no one about. He carried a pistol but no other weapon as did the others. It is one thing climbing over hilly land in daylight but quite another trying to find the way at night laden with heavy pots of gold and silver, and apprehensive of every sound. They did not speak but followed the slight twinkle of Beale's lantern some distance ahead. Occasionally a stone would be broken loose and would roll down, raising an unholy racket, and they would stand silently cursing themselves. But when they reached the place it was still dark and so they rested, stretching their cramped arms and hands.

It was bitterly cold, the wind searing through their clothing and biting their flesh. They were glad when there was enough light to start moving again. They cleared the hole's entrance of the brush and rubbish with which they had covered it the previous day. Then Beale had them lower him on the chain to take a look at the bottom. They had been unable to examine the depth of the hole the day before as they had no means of lowering themselves to the bottom. It appeared about seven or eight feet but Beale wanted to be absolutely sure. Some of these holes were made by streams which suddenly went underground and dried up. They didn't want to put the pots in and have them slide down into the bowels of the earth.

The ground was rocky and where there was earth it was filled with stones so that the sides of the hole were fairly stable and did not threaten Beale with a cave-in. But he decided it would be well to line the sides with some of the flat slabs of stone which were lying around.

As he got lower into the hole, Beale tested the bottom with his foot, still keeping his weight on the chain. There was a softness in the middle which suggested that it narrowed into a funnel which may or may not have a bottom. After probing awhile, Beale found that the slope of the bottom toward the middle would allow for several slabs of stone to be held firm enough to stand the weight of the pots. So, giving the signal to haul him up, Beale was soon out of the hole. The men dragged enough of the flat slabs of stone to line the sides and bottom up to the edge. These were lowered by using the chains and a nearby tree as a pulley. Then the pots were lowered and more slabs put on top.

They heard the sound of a rock falling just above them. Immediately they all froze. Who was it? No one up to any good would be in this place at this time. Their hands went to their pistols. They hadn't gone through all the hardships and danger to be done out of their treasure now. As long as he has no dog to smell us out, he won't find us, Beale thought. But just as he was thinking, a loud bark and excited panting heralded a large brown retriever.

"Come back, you fool dog, there ain't nothing over there." The dog turned and they prayed he'd go to his master. But no, he was a persistent animal and continued to stand in front of them and bark.

"D'ya hear me, come back here, damn you." But the dog took no notice. Beale was sweating. Why didn't the creature get out? The man shouted to the dog again and then they heard the footsteps get nearer. Beale thought quickly, nothing was going to stop the man. They could kill him but he hoped there would be no need.

Beckoning to the men, Beale walked toward the sounds the stranger was making. With any luck they could allay any suspicions and keep the man away from the hole.

"Over here, stranger, your dog's taken a dislike to us."

"Well, howdy. First time I ever saw strangers here at this time of day. What you up to?"

"We're not strangers, we're from these parts—but we've been on a hunting trip to the West. Only got in last night and we thought we'd take a look at our old haunts and see if there'd been much change. We've been away two years," Beale said.

"You don't mean it. And whereabouts were you?"

"In the West. Santa Fe was our farthest point. Ever been there yourself?" Beale was anxious to keep the man from asking too many questions.

"Naw, never been beyond Fincastle. I do a bit of trapping and hunting around these parts and that's enough for me. I'm on my own so I don't need much."

"Well, we're glad to meet you. My name's Beale."

"Mine's McGee. It's sure good to see you around. Gets a bit lonesome at times."

"Do you live around here?"

"Sure do—my cabin's just over the mountain. If you want to come back I can fix you some breakfast. I'm a pretty good cook."

"We were intending to visit with a man I used to know around here who had a cabin up near the Peaks of Otter. He

81

was named Jim Williams. Ever know him?" Beale tried to look convincing.

"No, never came across him. You going to stay there? I ain't seen no one living up near the Peaks and I've been hunting around here for a good many years."

"We're staying down at Buford's Tavern. Why don't you come and eat with us tonight?"

"I might do that too. I don't never go down there. But there's no reason I shouldn't." The man patted the dog who was sitting beside him watching the men closely.

Beale wished to God he'd get going and let them finish the job. They were edgy and ready to heave him down the mountain if he didn't clear out soon.

"We'd better get moving again," Beale said. "You going our way?" he asked the man as he started walking uphill followed by the men. Fortunately the stranger took the hint.

"I'm going to look at some traps I set, so I'll be moving along, but it was mighty good of you to ask me to eat with you. I'll be there later." And he started off away from them, followed by the dog.

Beale kept moving slowly up and away from the pots lest the man see them. They walked for some time and then doubled back as quietly as they could.

"That was a near one. I thought we were going to have to knock him out."

"He seemed harmless enough, but that dog's a sharp one. We'd better see that we cover up every trace of this morning's work," Beale replied.

They filled in the hole and laid several slabs of stone on the top, then covered this with leaves and rubbish so that it looked no different from the rest of the mountainside. They carried the wood and the chains with them and hid them far from the place before going back to Buford.

"Thank God it's done," Beale said as they sat by the

fire in the tavern waiting for something to eat. "We'll be able to rest easy now."

"I'm going to head for home after I've eaten," one of the men said. "I can deliver a few of the letters on my way." Those who stayed at the mine had given letters for their families to them when they left.

"I've got to stay around for a bit," Beale said. "I'll have to let you know when I'm ready to get back."

"We can find you here, can't we?"

"Yes, if I move on, I'll leave a message here. You know what I'm about. Tell any of the relatives to send letters here as we can pick them up on the way back."

"Wonder if the old man will come tonight?"

"I'll be here and I'll give him a good meal and plenty to drink. That'll keep him happy."

By the following week all except Beale and two men had left. He was waiting to hear more about Robert Morriss whom he thought would be the best person to entrust with the secret of the treasure. But in order to satisfy himself and the whole company, Beale intended to meet with him and to observe his manners and character. The other men had taken the wagons and hides to sell in Richmond, leaving Beale to do what was needed to find someone they could trust.

When Beale had talked with Thomas Jefferson before setting out for the West, the former President had invited Beale to call upon him when he got back and report on his travels. Jefferson was now 76 years old but he was in good physical health except for some rheumatism. His mind was as keen as ever and he was constantly busy with the University of Virginia, going every day to supervise the builders. He also was working on a scheme of elementary education for the poor.

Much of the bitterness of his political enemies had

turned to respect and even reverence, yet he was as modest and approachable as before. Even so, Beale was reluctant to add to the constant stream of visitors who called on Jefferson at Monticello. Sometimes as many as fifty people stayed overnight. Jefferson was so hospitable, hating to turn anyone away, that he had emptied his purse and deprived himself and his family in order to provide for the never-ending visitors. They came from all over the world to see him and to talk about politics, philosophy, science, architecture, democracy, music and literature. Inventors brought their plans to him and he was always happy to see them, as Jefferson's curious mind was constantly searching for improvement in all things. Jefferson was working on various inventions of his own, and one, a polygraph, proved helpful in answering some of the tremendous correspondence which he carried on with so many different people. Jefferson's grandson, Thomas Jefferson Randolph, found a file of 16,000 answers to correspondents written by his grandfather when he was going through his papers after his death.

Jefferson was a kind of national monument now. People would go to Monticello and stand around just to look at him. Sometimes he would have to flee to Poplar Forest in order to get a little quiet to work and read. At Poplar Forest he was not troubled with so many visitors, and Beale thought this was the best place to try to see Jefferson.

When he heard that Jefferson would be there the week before Christmas, Beale arranged to ride there a few days ahead of the other men and then meet with them so they could all ride to Lynchburg together.

Jefferson received Beale with his usual friendliness and was extremely interested in all he had to tell him. Beale did not mention the gold and silver but he talked at length about the country, the Indians, about their stay near Santa Fe and about the type of trees, shrubs and flowers found in the different parts of the country.

Knowing that Jefferson was setting up a small museum and was interested in obtaining various things for exhibit there, Beale had brought several pieces of Indian jewelry and headdresses. Jefferson was very glad to accept them and gave Beale several maps and a small compass in return.

When Beale left Poplar Forest to meet with his men, the weather changed abruptly. The skies turned leaden and he could see that snow was in the air. When he reached the tavern which was their rendezvous, he found them waiting for him.

"We're in for bad weather, Tom. Better stay the night here, I think."

"You're right. We're not in a great hurry. It may clear up by tomorrow."

But the next day was worse, the wind rose and the snow froze hard on the ground. It continued to storm and the road was too deep in snow for the horses to get through. So they made themselves comfortable and waited for a thaw.

Buford's Gap

8.

It was early in January when Beale and two others went to Lynchburg with the intention of making the acquaintance of Robert Morriss. Lynchburg, which some still called by its old name of Lynch Ferry, was a growing place. Although New London was the county seat its population had been declining since the Revolution as many Scottish merchants had refused to take the oath of allegiance to the new American government and had packed up and gone to Canada. The river transportation was increasing and Lynchburg was building up considerable trade, outdoing New London.

It was because Robert Morriss saw this changing growth that he had come to Lynchburg originally and had decided to stay and open a hotel. Although he was too gentle and honest to make a vast fortune, he and his wife prospered and the hotel had a good reputation among the better class of traveler and the gentry of the area.

Beale was glad to find that the Washington Hotel was a comfortable place offering excellent accommodations for a few days. Later, two of them were going to visit relatives near Richmond but he might stay through the winter if the hunting was good.

Morriss was glad to have the company of the three men. Being a gentleman himself, and of good education, it gave him considerable pleasure to have men who could converse with him on a wide range of subjects. For Beale this meant they could keep off the subject of themselves and their plans, and learn much about the character and temperament of their host. Robert Morriss was 41 at this time and his wife a few years younger. They took a liking to Beale and his friends almost immediately.

Mrs. Morriss, a small, gentle and accomplished woman, found Beale's physical appearance and immense vitality overpowering at first. He was six feet tall and very muscular from hard work and long journeying. The sun had burned his skin, giving him a swarthy appearance which was accentuated by his black eyes and hair. But Beale's friendly disposition and courteous manner toward her soon won Mrs. Morriss over.

In fact all three men were included quickly in the social life of the community, the ladies favoring them with attentions and fluttering admiration. Beale let them know that he and his men were hunters and were staying only a short while as they intended to go on another hunting expedition as soon as the winter was over.

It did not take the men long to decide that Morriss was the man they could trust with their secret; but to make doubly sure, after his friends left for Richmond, Beale stuck to his original plan of staying in the hotel for the winter so that he could observe Morriss over a period of time.

Beale made a friend of an elderly man who seemed to make his home in the hotel. This man, Gilbert Ewing, had occupied a small room on an upper floor for a number of years. He was quiet and unobtrusive with an unworldly expression of suppressed sadness. Mostly he helped the Morrisses with bookkeeping and letter-writing from time to time. Beale made a point of talking to him and gaining his confidence so that he might get Ewing's opinion of the Morrisses.

"They've been very good to me," Ewing said. "I don't know what would have become of me if they hadn't helped me. I lost my business and my wife died and I didn't have anything left. But they took me in and let me live here without charge in return for the paltry bit of bookkeeping or letter-writing I can do. I hope God rewards them. They deserve it, I only wish I had the means to pay them back."

"I don't think they expect payment. The work you do is a great help to them," Beale said.

Ewing sighed. "I can't seem to keep myself in good health. If it isn't one thing it's another and that's what stops me from doing more."

"Have you known the Morrisses for many years?"

"Yes, I knew them when they first came here. They came from Loudoun county. That's where he met Mrs. Morriss—Sarah Mitchell she was then. Right pretty she was. Mr. Morriss set up as a purchaser and shipper of tobacco in a bigger way than had been known in these parts. He did well, too, making a good bit of money. He was honest and everyone respected him. They had a big house on Main Street, all built of brick, one of the first of its kind in the area. Mrs. Morriss was always helping people one way or another and if anyone was sick she came around with her little basket of homemade cakes or some flowers or fresh fruit from her garden."

"She was a good woman, then."

"Yes, she helped her husband without his knowing what she was up to. I had my own little business then. A book shop. Not very big but it was just right for us; we did everything ourselves. Then my wife got sick and I tried to look after her and the shop at the same time. But it was too much for me and it went down and I had to sell for next to nothing. It gave me enough for the funeral and nothing else. That's when the Morrisses first helped me. I asked them for a job—any job—but he said they had losses and he couldn't offer much. In fact he said he would have to give up the house and try something else as his business was finished."

"Ewing paused and Beale asked, "How did the Morrisses lose their money?"

"Tobacco was high and he thought it would go higher so he bought a good deal at a price that fairly ruined him. Then before he could collect, the price dropped right down and he had to sell for what he could get."

"Was that why he started the hotel?"

"Yes. Mrs. Morriss was wonderful about it. They say it was Mrs. Morriss's idea and she talked him into leasing it. She never complained about the work, though she had never lifted a finger before. She kept a smiling face and welcomed the visitors so that all the best people came here. And they didn't forget me neither. They asked me to come and keep the books, but I knew they needed someone who could do a right smart job. They couldn't afford to leave the books in the hands of a business failure. So I told them I couldn't do bookkeeping. And then they asked me to help around the place and that's what I've done ever since. They've been mighty good to me and I'm glad to tell you about it. Fine people they are. Pity there's not more like them in the world."

He sighed heavily, then smiled as Beale signaled to the waiter to refill their glasses.

It seemed that the Morrisses were esteemed by rich and poor alike. Wherever he went in town, Beale heard only good about them. Now he could rest easy; all the company would surely be pleased to trust Morriss with the secret. He began casting around in his mind for some way of entrusting the secret to Morriss without revealing it. It would have to be in code. Most people had their own code which they changed every so often. Nobody wanted his letters read by the carriers—who could tell what secrets would be revealed if

90

someone offered enough money? The mails were few and people in most isolated districts arranged for letters to be carried by anyone going anywhere near the destination.

Beale had no code of his own; he hadn't needed one up to now. He knew Mr. Jefferson had a code which was to have been used by Lewis and Clark on their expedition. He could use that, but someone might recognize it and then all would be lost. The best thing was to work out his own. He had time—after all he had to get the agreement of the company before he could do any more.

9.

The journey back proved far worse than they had expected. Beale had kept a careful chart on their way from the mine to St. Louis and if it hadn't been for this they never would have found their way back. As it was it took them a full month longer than they planned and they realized that their luck would not hold forever; their next trip might be their last.

"Next time I'm on this trail I'll be on my way home for good," one of the men remarked.

"I was thinking the same thing," Beale answered." If all's well at the camp we should have enough of the stuff to last our lifetime by now." Beale had put into words what was lurking in the minds of all of them.

"I hope to God nothing's happened to them."

"We'll soon know. If my reckoning's right, we should be there in a couple of days," Beale said.

"They'll be watching for us, I reckon."

And indeed they were. Those at the mine were as fearful of harm coming to Beale's party as the returning party had been of those they left behind. The men at the camp had kept watch for the past month and although their greetings were casual, the hard grip of the hand, the clearing of the throat betrayed their pent-up emotion.

A quick glance around told Beale that all was well. Charlie, beaming, whispered that the gold was holding out well and looked as if it would go on forever.

They ate heartily of the spit-roasted lamb and corn while everyone tried to question them at the same time about their wives and relatives and the state of things in Virginia. Then Beale passed out the letters.

This was the first word most of them had had in nearly three years. One or two held the letters for a while without breaking the seal as if fearful of what might be inside. Others tore them open, greedy for news whatever it might be.

Beale had brought provisions from St. Louis and that night they had a feast. They had been living on game, corn and beans for several months now and their stomachs were crying for bread and a variety of food.

The men were more hungry for news than food though. Every detail was of interest. Beale realized how lonely they were for their own kind, especially women. Perhaps they should go back with what gold they had while they were alive and able to enjoy it, he thought. But the men would have none of it.

"We don't have enough yet. There's plenty here to make millionaires of us all if we stay long enough to get it out."

So they slipped back into the routine of work and more work—digging, washing, cracking the ore and storing away the metal. Some of the original Indians were still there. Some had left and others had taken their place. Beale regretted ever bringing the Indians in. He knew they would betray them eventually, but they substantially increased the amount of metal mined each day and so far they had been loyal enough. But would it last?

A cold shiver of warning sounded in Beale's mind—they must get out soon—greed was trying their luck too hard. They had enough. Not one of them need ever work again unless he wanted to. Then Beale stopped himself with a jerk. God, what's come over me? Surely we can keep a few Indians under control. All we have to do is keep our eyes peeled and stop any funny business before it gets started. After all we have gone through we might as well get all we can. We've earned it. So, Beale made the fateful decision that was to affect the lives of the whole company.

There was a dreadful sameness about their days which seemed more apparent than before and it took its toll on the men. They worked with an inhuman intensity that was almost frightening. Joe tried to remonstrate with them. "Take it easy," he'd say, "you don't have to work your guts out."

And Beale replied for all of them, "We'll take it easy when we get home." Then he realized he had no home and no one waiting for him. He cursed himself for letting it matter to him. There were plenty of women in the world and with all this gold they'd all belong to him. And he worked more feverishly and more intensely than any of them.

After they'd eaten in the evening they'd sit around the fire and ask questions: "How did it look back there? What was going on in Williamsburg and Philadelphia? They'd talk nostalgically of the Blue Ridge, how the dawn showed on the mountains and how the valley looked in sunshine and rain. Then the talk would go to women and after a while they'd fall silent one by one, each wrapped in his own particular fantasy.

One night Joe came to Beale and said, "I think you should drop that rule about Indian women. It's not natural for men to go so long without touching a female. It's either squaws or go to Santa Fe. There's going to be trouble with some of 'em if something isn't done. They're working too hard and they're all wound up. Those that went with you came back with tales of all the women they'd had and it's sort of unsettled the others and set them thinking about things they'd best forget—while they're here anyhow."

95

"They're not complaining. I told you before it's too dangerous to get mixed up with squaws for more reasons than one, and it's a mighty long trip back to Santa Fe. There's no guarantee they'd get anything there. Those Spanish and Mexicans might not be as friendly as they were three years ago," Beale replied.

"I wouldn't know about that, but I do know men can't go on so long without some kind of relaxation. They're not complaining because they don't know how near the breaking point they are, or if they do they won't admit it. If you were finishing up in the next month or two it wouldn't matter; but if they're going on for another couple of years, you'd better make a change."

"You may be right, Joe, but I'm doing it my way for a while longer."

Joe shrugged. "Don't forget I warned you."

It must have been about three months later that shots ripped open the sleeping group. Beale was up in an instant, gun in hand. But it was so dark that it was impossible to see anything. Where's that damned guard? he thought. What fool would be shooting in the dark? Not Indians. By now the night was alive. Someone stirred up the fire and the blaze showed Beale a bunch of men trying to hold down a struggling figure.

"What's going on?" he demanded, "let's get some light here." Thrusting himself into the group he saw they had pinned to the ground a man nicknamed Shorty.

"He shot Joe," one of the men said in explanation.

"Joe! Is he all right?"

"He's dead."

"Dead!" An icy hand clutched Beale's throat. "Where is he?" He touched Shorty with his foot. "Tie him up, I'll deal with him later."

Joe had been shot in the heart at close range. Powder

burns on his shirt showed where the bullet had entered. Beale knelt down and held the already cooling wrist. There was no pulse, but he couldn't believe Joe was dead.

"Bring the lantern nearer," he said as he lifted the lids that someone had closed over the sightless eyes. A sob ripped out of his throat. This man had been with him through the War of 1812. They'd suffered more than one bloody cam-paign—and now to die like this. Joe had been a good and loyal friend. Rage swept through Beale as he got to his feet. "Do any of you know how this came about?"

There was silence, then someone said, "I was sleeping. It was the shot that wakened me."

"I was on the other side."

"It was too dark to see anything."

Beale saw it was unlikely that he could get any help from them. "Bring Shorty over to the fire," Beale said, "I'll get it out of him."

They loosened the rope on Shorty's legs and brought him over. He was silent and subdued. He looked dazed, his eyes staring at nothing.

"What have you got to say for yourself?" Beale demanded, his voice grimly controlled. The man said nothing. Beale waited then said, "Did you shoot Joe?"

Suddenly Shorty lunged at Beale, shrieking a jumble of unintelligible words. The man nearest him was knocked side-ways into the fire with the sudden violence of Shorty's lunge, but Beale held him a fraction of a second and then threw him to the ground where four men held him down. Shorty was still shouting and struggling, and, in spite of his anger over Joe's death Beale realized that Shorty was out of his mind.

"Better tie him up again, he can't tell us anything now," Beale said.

He ordered a swig of their precious whiskey for every man, but no one could sleep. Shorty was alternately shouting

97

or silent. It was unnerving to have his frenzied shouts break the silence and echo through the hills. Beale stayed by Joe's body, and as soon as it was light he helped wash him and dress him in his old black suit. Joe had brought along this suit for what he called his socializing occasions. Anything approaching a formal event, whether it be a wedding or a funeral, rated a black suit in Joe's mind. The harsh anger blinded Beale as he remembered the last time Joe had worn the suit. Why should a good man who had spent his life on other people come to an end like this in this lonely barren place so far from the hills he loved? Joe had always wanted to be buried in the blue shadows of the Peaks of Otter where he had spent most of his life. Joe was the only man who had not been able to put up his full share of money into the expedition. But no one cared because they needed his medical experience and because he was a unifier of men; someone good to have around; someone who took the meanness out of others. They all had wanted Joe to have an equal share, and now he never would get any. Now he was dead. Killed by one of his friends. Shot in the dark. Why?

They buried him the next day. Beale blamed himself bitterly for not taking more heed of what Joe had told him about some of the men being near breaking point, but he hadn't mentioned any names. Shorty had not shown any signs of breaking before this. Or had he? Now Beale remembered that Shorty had been picking on Joe and he'd seemed very argumentative at times. Other times he'd gone off on his own not speaking to anyone. But this happened to everyone didn't it? Or was it a sign of a breakdown? Were they all on the edge? Should he insist they go back?

But when he brought the subject up, there were only three who wanted to stop now and return home. Like Beale, they were held by the gold.

Beale was never the same after this incident. He was

bitterly resentful about Joe's death. Not only was Joe the only man with medical experience but he had been the friend of everyone. The fact that Shorty was still out of his mind so that Beale could get nothing out of him made it worse. They had to take turns watching over Shorty. He couldn't be kept tied up all the time. He had to be fed and exercised like an animal. Shorty was in a strange state. He was no longer screaming or struggling; he was quiet but it was the quiet of waiting. There was a watchfulness about him that was scary. The men were nervous around him, expecting him to become violent without warning. It was a strain on all of them, yet there was nothing to be done about it; they couldn't let him starve.

At times Beale thought Shorty was improving. He would act almost normal for a while; then he would lapse into his weird, watchful silences again and Beale knew there was no improvement after all. Every night a man had to sleep with Shorty, or rather to watch over him. They took it in turns so it was only one night a month, but it weighed heavily on them.

No one knew whether Shorty had killed in cold blood or in self-defense. Sometimes they would try to get him to tell, but he never gave anything away.

"If he didn't feel guilty he'd tell us about it," one man said to Beale. "He must be as guilty as hell or he'd say something to put himself straight with us. We ought to shoot him and put him out of his misery and save ourselves all this nursemaiding."

"We can't find him guilty without hearing his side," said Beale, "we've no proof that he shot to kill."

So they went on caring for Shorty, hoping he'd get his wits back pretty soon. An uneasy feeling was alive in the camp and men began watching each other, wondering who might be stricken next.

Then one morning Shorty was missing. The man

watching in his tent had fallen asleep and Shorty must have taken this opportunity to get away. His ankles were tied only loosely at night so he could easily get free if no one was watching.

"He can't have got far," Beale said, "we'll take some men and search for him. We ought to find him in a few hours at most."

"You not find him," Charlie said, "he gone with Indian on horse. I see trail."

"Show me," Beale answered.

Charlie led Beale along behind Shorty's tent and pointed to the faint marks on the ground where Shorty had dragged himself along until he got free of the ropes around his ankles.

"Here marks of pony. Two of them." And sure enough Beale could see the hoof marks in the ground.

"Who was it? I didn't know he was friendly with the Indians."

"He talk of bringing squaw in his tent. Maybe she come for him," Charlie said softly, looking off into the distance.

"What do you mean? Do you know that Shorty did this?"

"He talk about it. I don't know what Mr. Shorty did."

"Well, from these marks he went willingly, so we don't have to worry about that. In a way it's easier for us without him."

"He no good sick man. You need strong well men like yourself, master."

Beale called off the search. There was no point in chasing after the Indian. If Shorty went willingly he wouldn't want to be dragged back. Secretly all the men were relieved to be without Shorty. The strain of caring for him was too much on top of the work in the gold camp.

Charlie continued, "Good riddance, I say. We couldn't go on taking care of him forever."

Beale didn't answer. Really he felt the same way but

hesitated to make it obvious. After all, Shorty was a shareholder in the company and they had a responsibility to him just as they had to all the others. Beale was also worried about what Shorty might do. Was he out for revenge? Or was he just a poor lunatic hopelessly out of his mind?

Beale also thought about what Charlie had hinted. Was he warning him? Perhaps I should have listened to Joe, he thought; he knew a great deal about men. After much consideration Beale decided to let a company of men go with Charlie to Santa Fe. After all, they needed provisions and Santa Fe was nearer than St. Louis.

Ten men were chosen by lot to make the journey. The ten who went with Beale did not enter the lottery. They could enter after two years if they were still here. Those going expected to be gone about a month and they intended to have a good time.

Beale had warned them that they might expect trouble when they reached Santa Fe. A good many changes might have taken place and their friends might be gone or dead. The men took some of the buffalo hides with them for trading and to show proof that they were hunting. Not a word was to be said about the gold. Beale sent messages t' the ladies of La Conchita and to Senor Gomez.

It was strange in the camp without Charlie. He had never lost his sense of humor throughout the whole time. Charlie was always ready with some bit of wisdom or wit whenever things got too strained. Around the fire at night he would tell tales of his ancestors, all of whom were either kings or pirates; and keep their minds off the bitter wind that blew off the mountains. Losing Shorty was such a relief that the men were in good humor and things went a lot smoother than they had for a long time. There was more camaraderie and a return to the easy relationships of earlier days.

During the time they had been working the vein, they had gradually built snug cabins for themselves. Using buffalo hides and poles cut from trees, some had made good-sized rooms divided by curtains of soft antelope skin. Others had used the tent method, and some made caves in the hillside and built another room of hides in front. When their blankets had shown signs of wear they had simply replaced them with skins. They were so used to sleeping this way that they would feel strange in beds with sheets and pillows. Often they would dream of a soft warm bed scented by some beautiful female who lay waiting for them, and they would wake determined to work harder so that they could get back with enough to keep them in such luxuries forever.

Such things as soap, razors, combs, paper, pens and needles and thread were very scarce and precious. They used them very sparingly. Their friends, even their wives, would have found it hard to recognize these men if they had come upon them in the camp. Their moustaches and beards had grown long. As their clothing had torn or worn thin they had patched it with whatever was handy, sometimes cloth, sometimes skin. Beale had brought back supplies of many things from St. Louis but there was not enough for all. They hoped to get more from Santa Fe. No one complained though, and no one seemed to think it ironic that with all the gold they had, they were short of even the smallest luxuries.

To make up for the men who had gone to Santa Fe, Beale took on about fifteen more Indians and kept them working as long as daylight lasted. Soon they were bringing out almost double the amount of precious metals as before. But there was never enough to satisfy the men. If the moon was bright enough they would even work by night, adding and adding to the store.

10.

Charlie and his party had little difficulty finding the route back to Santa Fe. The horses were in good condition and the men were sustained by the excitement of seeing a human habitation again after so long. The hard labor they had been engaged in made the traveling seem easy although it was rough and arduous going.

Remembering their difficulties with the police last time, they camped some 30 miles from Santa Fe and made a plan for entering and finding out what sort of a welcome they might expect.

"There used to be some Indians camping to the southwest. If they're still there we could find out something from them without risking our necks," one of the men suggested.

"No see Indian fire," Charlie said. "I think I go see then come back tell you. I Mexican and they not touch me."

So it was agreed, and they waited impatiently as Charlie rode off. He hadn't been gone more than three hours when they saw him galloping back waving at them excitedly.

"The Mexicans, my people, have the city. It is ours. The Spaniards are gone. All are welcome. Come, quick!"

It was true. The Mexicans had thrown off Spanish rule and were welcoming all traders and other visitors to the city. There was an entirely different spirit in the place. Gone was

103

the silent hostility, the sideways glance, the fearful whisper. All was fiesta.

This was a break the men hadn't dreamed of. Lying that night in the comfortable beds and soft sheets they had been dreaming of so long, they thought of their comrades back at the mine and felt a little guilty. But this didn't last long. The friendly arms and warm soft lips of the hot-blooded Mexican girls wiped out thought of anything else but the delicious moment. The hides had sold well, so they had plenty of money and the girls were more than willing to help them spend it. They liked these unkempt men who were so surprisingly grateful. Underneath the rough beards and hard, sunbaked skin, they found gentle, courteous men who could be wildly passionate but were always generous.

The two weeks they intended to stay stretched out into three and then four. After all, they had to take time to buy supplies. They got a new wagon to carry back all they had bought. They felt they ought to make up to the others some way or another. Senora Conchita sent gifts of homemade cakes and cheeses and preserves to Beale as well as several silken shirts. They bought boots and other clothing with the idea that they would like to look more presentable when they touched civilization again.

The men who had not yet had a chance to get away from the camp got first pick of everything and the promise of staying twice as long as the others. It certainly had lifted morale to hear about the changes in Santa Fe and to get all the fresh provisions. And there was no doubt that there is no substitute for a woman.

The treasure continued to mount and in the Fall of 1821 it was decided that another journey back must be made to make another deposit of gold and silver in the hiding place. This was to be the last. When Beale returned they would all travel back together with the remaining metal.

This time Beale was to leave instructions in code with Robert Morriss to safeguard the relatives of the men should anything happen to them, and then head straight back.

The thought of another terrible journey like the last did not appeal to Beale, but he knew the trail better than anyone else and he was the only one who knew Robert Morriss. Also he was the only one that everybody trusted. So he had to go. The men who had not been either to Santa Fe or to Virginia went with him. They took two wagons again and hid the gold under skins in the same way as before. The only difference was that they stopped in St. Louis this time because one of the wagons was damaged and needed repairs.

Beale therefore decided to visit his old friend, Monsieur Pierre, and ask his help. He felt he could trust him. Accordingly he sought him out and found him much the same, a little older and more shriveled up but as sharp and brilliant as ever.

"It is a great pleasure to have you here again, Captain Beale," he said. "I wondered what happened to you."

"I did pretty well, but as you know it is a long and dangerous trip and took more time than we expected. I passed through two years ago, but as I was in a hurry I did not stop although I was sorely tempted to come and renew acquaintance with you."

"Can I be of any assistance this time, Captain?"

"I need another wagon and would be glad if you could tell me where I could obtain one. One of ours is in bad shape."

"Why not sell your skins here? We are good traders, you know." Monsieur Pierre smiled. "We will give you a good price and you will not have so much to transport."

Beale's mind worked quickly. Now that they were over the worst it would be easier traveling with one wagon. They each had their horses and they would have the extra animals from the damaged wagon if they sold it.

"What would you trade with?"

"What do you want? We have many things available here."

"Do you have jewels? Some of us have wives and relatives we have to please after being away so long. We could trade for these, maybe." Beale was cautious.

"Jewels!" Monsieur Pierre was surprised. "It takes many good skins for one jewel, you know Captain. How many do you have?"

"Not enough, as we must take some with us. We promised them to traders in Lynchburg and Richmond. But we have a little gold."

"Gold!" Monsieur Pierre's eyes narrowed. "That is a different matter."

"Show me the jewels and tell me the price and I will tell you if we have enough to trade," Beale said. "You understand, of course, we do not want anyone to know we have gold. We might not keep it long if others knew. And we worked hard for it. We traded many a skin in Santa Fe to get it."

"Traded in Santa Fe! God's body, Captain, Santa Fe hasn't been trading for years."

"You are mistaken. I have good news for you. The Mexicans have taken their city back from the Spaniards and they are willing to trade with anyone."

Monsieur Pierre was excited at last. His eyes sparkled. "This is most wonderful news. Have you told anyone else?"

"No, we have just come. You can take full advantage and get a trading mission off before anyone else does."

"How can I repay you?"

"By trading me the jewels and keeping quiet about my business."

"That I would do in any case." Monsieur Pierre looked hurt.

"I know. It was just my way of saying that I do not want

anything in return for this information. I owe you much more than I can ever repay you for your kindness in finding Hawk Eye as our guide. Without him we would have been dead by now."

Monsieur Pierre smiled. "Gratitude is rare in this hard world, Captain Beale, and I honor and thank you for it."

Beale made a good trade with Monsieur Pierre, exchanging some metal and a few hides for $13,000 worth of jewels. These were easy to transport and saved taking the second wagon.

When they reached Buford in December, 1821 they followed much the same pattern as before and disposed of the pots of metal, amounting to 1,907 pounds of gold and 1,288 pounds of silver, and the jewels in the same hiding place as the other.

Then Beale settled down to devising a code that would safeguard the treasure and yet make it possible for Robert Morriss to find it should anything happen to himself and the men.

Beale had made the same arrangements for the men as the last time: they went on to their friends and relatives to wait for a message from him to tell them when to start out again. However, Beale did not linger in Buford this time. He went straight on to Robert Morriss's hotel in Lynchburg with the intention of working out the codes and a method of keeping them safe.

The Morrisses were surprised and pleased to see Beale again and made him very comfortable with a quiet sitting room and bedroom of his own. Beale told them he had come to settle some business and to trade the hides and skins they had brought back from the western plains. He also hoped to do some hunting in the area if the weather permitted.

This time Beale found himself the center of attraction. The ladies remembered him from his last visit and were happy to renew the acquaintance of so dashing a figure.

107

Beale was even more sunburned and romantic looking than before. He was in fine physical shape, lean and hard, but with the same courteous manners toward the ladies and the same arrogant, careless way of dealing with lesser men who tried to take advantage of him.

To the ladies he was more fascinating than before. They were all falling over themselves to invite him to parties of all kinds. Hand-knitted gloves, socks and mufflers were pressed upon him and embroidered waistcoats and fancy slippers arrived by messenger until his chest was full. Beale accepted them all with a bow and a wicked smile; it was far easier than refusing. This time he did not pay attentions or dally with any particular lady. He had too much to do.

11.

    Beale tried a good many different methods before he finally decided on the type of information he would leave for Morriss. Before anything could be coded it had to be set out in clear English. Beale wanted it to be brief and yet to give enough information it would run to several pages. After much thought he settled on the idea of writing three separate messages. This was a safeguard should the messages fall into the wrong hands. One message would state the amount of the treasure and when it was buried. Another would tell where it was buried, with instructions for getting it out. And the third would tell the names of those relatives and friends who were the beneficiaries of the men should they never return.

    Beale did not number the messages, so no one could tell which was which unless he had the key. Then he started to put them in code. Beale wanted to use a key that would be familiar and accessible to Robert Morriss, and yet one which would not occur immediately to an unauthorized person.

    Beale and Morriss had spent many an evening discussing the country and the turn politics was taking. Each was an admirer of Thomas Jefferson and upheld him and his radical views against the more conservative friends who came to the hotel. Robert Morriss was also a Mason and understood the importance of the number three. So with all these things in mind Beale chose certain documents that were familiar to both of them. A namesake of Robert Morriss had been one of the signers of the Declaration of Independence, so Beale decided to use that document as the key to one of the messages.

The first time he started coding by numbering each letter of the Declaration of Independence and substituting the number for the letters of the words in the message. But this ran into such a large number of different numbers that it was clumsy and space-consuming. So he numbered each word of the Declaration and used only the first letter from each word. He cut down the messages until he had only the barest information in each and decided to write details in letters which he would send to Morriss later.

The messages were so written that each contained only part of the information required to get the treasure. The first referred only to the vault or excavation and did not say what was in the vault, so that any unauthorized person might not consider it of any great significance. The second told exactly what is hidden but not where, and the third gave the names of relatives in code so that no unauthorized person could use the name of any of the party and persuade Morriss to give him the key, or to defraud any of the true beneficiaries. Weeks of painstaking work went into this coding until Beale was satisfied that no one could get the treasure without the keys. He then waited a while, considering when he would give them to Morriss and how best to impress their value upon him without divulging more than was necessary. For if Beale and his men returned safely there was no need for anyone, not even Morriss, to know the secret contained in the messages. The fewer who knew about the treasure the better.

Beale now had a sheaf of papers containing his messages, which looked like a series of disjointed numbers and conveyed nothing of value to the casual observer. To prevent damage by fire or careless handling he placed them in an iron box for safety. He felt they would be safe there until he decided what to do with them next.

Several times he considered telling Morriss the whole story, feeling sure he could trust him completely. But then he reconsidered and decided to give Morriss the locked iron box with the three coded messages inside, as well as the two letters concerning them, and ask him to keep it safely for him.

Robert Morriss was perfectly willing to take care of the locked box, thinking it contained papers or valuables which Beale did not want to carry around with him. "I'll take good care of it for you, but I hope you'll soon be back to claim it. We like having you here with us, don't we my dear?" Morriss turned to his wife who had just come into the room.

"Of course we do. We will miss you very much, Captain Beale, and so will all the other ladies in Lynchburg."

"You are very kind, ma'am. You have made my stay here so comfortable that it's hard to take my leave, but I have to get back to the West."

"I wish you a safe journey and a speedy return. You know we will be glad to have you here any time you can come. Now I must go to see what is happening in the kitchens and I know you men have business to talk about, so you will excuse me." Mrs. Morriss smiled and left them alone again.

"You are fortunate in having such an admirable wife," Beale remarked.

"Yes, I am indeed. I hope you will be equally fortunate."

"I have no time for a wife in the business I'm in," Beale replied, and then went on quickly, "I have an observation concerning the box you are to take care of for me. It is very valuable and if I should not return, will you open it after ten years have passed and carry out the instructions that are

111

given in the two letters you will find inside?"

"I will carry them out to the letter and I give you my word that you need not have a moment's uneasiness regarding the box. I will tell no one about it unless anything happens to me which would prevent my continuing to take care of it. Then I will choose some suitable person whom I can trust and ask him to carry out your wishes."

"Thank you, but don't let it leave your hands unless there is no other way, will you?"

"No, I will not. But you will be back within a year or two, won't you?"

"I expect to be back in two years but the journey is hazardous and there are a good many dangers—Indians, grizzlies, robbers, as well as floods and storms which I have to consider and take some precautions against. Our luck has held pretty well, but it will not hold forever."

Beale looked serious and then he laughed. "I sound like an old woman. It's just that I promised the rest of the men that I would take these steps to ensure that their relatives are taken care of should anything happen to them. That's why I have taken so much trouble and why I am so concerned about the box. It contains information that affects the lives and well-being of many people."

"I understand perfectly and you can assure them that all will be done as you have asked. Now let us drink to your journey and a safe return." Morriss beckoned to one of the serving men to bring them glasses and wine. Then he said, "You will take the key of the box with you, I hope."

"Yes, as a safeguard, but if it should be necessary you can open it by breaking the lock."

After emptying their glasses, Beale mounted his horse and was on his way to Buford's Tavern where he expected to meet with the rest of the party before starting back to the West.

12.

From the very beginning of their trip back to the gold camp Beale had the uneasy feeling that luck was against them. They were delayed by several bad storms and one of the horses went lame. In St. Louis they had difficulty getting supplies. The news that Santa Fe was open for trade had spread around and several groups were buying up goods hoping to sell them at an immense profit. Up to now, surplus flour and furs had been sold in New Orleans where the prices given were not good. The prospect of a new market for the manufactured goods they could obtain in exchange for their furs in New Orleans excited the traders and those who wanted to invest their money with them.

Beale noticed a great deal of difference in St. Louis since they had been there first in 1817. St. Louis was growing fast. There were about 115 buildings now and a population of roughly 3,000. The state of Missouri was expected to incorporate St. Louis as a city this year, 1822. There was an air of importance about the place and a feeling of growth and virility. The *Louisiana Gazette* was printed regularly and a small printer had published a number of books. Also a private company had been responsible for providing two fire engines, primitive but necessary safeguards for the wooden houses that were easy prey to fire.

They stayed several days in St. Louis and there Beale

wrote a long letter to Robert Morriss. He was worried lest Morriss not understand the value of the box. Beale had placed instructions concerning the codes in the box but he felt Morriss should have some idea of what was in it. So on May 9, 1822 he wrote:

Robt. Morriss, Esq.,

My esteemed friend,

"Ever since leaving my comfortable quarters at your house I have been journeying to this place and only succeeded in reaching it yesterday. I have had, altogether, a pleasant time, the weather being fine and the atmosphere bracing. I shall remain here a week or ten days longer, then "ho" for the plains, to hunt buffalo and encounter the savage grizzlies. How long I may be absent I cannot now determine, certainly not less than two years, perhaps longer.

"With regard to the box left in your charge I have a few words to say, and, if you will permit me, give you some instructions concerning it. It contains papers vitally affecting the fortunes of myself and many others engaged in business with me, and in the event of my death its loss might be irreparable. You will, therefore, see the necessity of guarding it with vigilance and care to prevent so great a catastrophe. It also contains some letters addressed to yourself and which will be necessary to enlighten you concerning the business in which we are engaged.

"Should none of us ever return you will please preserve carefully the box for a period of ten years from the date of this letter, and if I or no one in authority from me, during that time demands its restoration, you will open it, which can be done by removing the lock.

"You will find, in addition to the papers addressed to you, other papers which will be unintelligible without the aid of a key to assist you. Such a key I have left in the hands of a friend in this place, sealed, addressed to yourself and endorsed 'Not to be delivered until June, 1832'. By means of this you will understand fully all you will be required to do.

"I know you will cheerfully comply with this request, thus adding to the many obligations under which you have already placed me. In the meantime should death or sickness happen to you, to which all are liable, please select from among your friends some one worthy, and to him hand this letter, and to him delegate your authority.

"I have been thus particular in my instructions in consequence of the somewhat perilous enterprise in which we are engaged, but trust we shall meet long ere the time expires, and so save you the trouble. Be the result what it may, however, the game is worth the candle and we will play it to the end.

"With kindest wishes for your most excellent wife, compliments to the ladies, a good word to enquiring friends, if there be any, and assurances of my highest esteem for yourself, I remain as ever,

Your sincere friend

Tho^S. Jeff^n. Beale."

After he had sealed the letter and arranged for its transportation, Beale felt a great load off his mind. Nothing could go wrong now. Morriss would know from this letter that the box must be kept safe at all costs, and it was with a lighter heart that he started out across the plains again.

Although this was the fifth time Beale had crossed it, the vast stretches of land with oceans of undulating grass never ceased to strike awe in Beale's mind. The majesty of such immensity under the blue arch of the sky seemed as if it belonged to another planet. It gave him a feeling of reverence for nature and its creator.

It was June when they arrived at the camp. The men looked thin and tense. Their skin was burnt to a leathery

115

toughness that made them look like old men. There was a feverish glitter in their eyes that Beale had not noticed before. I suppose it's being away so long that's made me notice it, Beale thought as they greeted each other. This time the letters from home did not all contain good news. One man's wife had died, and another had lost a child, and two had been forced to leave their homesteads. It's time to go back, Beale thought; four years is a long time to be away when there's a family waiting. But the gold held out—the vein seemed even richer—and so they decided to keep working for at least another year. It seemed as if the gold possessed them and would not let them go. The yellow glitter reflected in their eyes and on their skin, they ate less and slept only when there was no light to work by. If the moon was up, Beale would see men working by its light; it was as if the gold would not let them rest as long as there was the slightest bit of light.

There was less talking than there used to be. It was rare for anyone to smile. All energy went into the gold which sucked their vitality and demanded total allegiance. Those who had been to Santa Fe had brought back more iron pots to stow away the ore and several of these had been filled since Beale left. He had to be very watchful left the horses be neglected as the men considered time away from the gold wasted and would escape the chores if they could.

Day followed day of unceasing monotony. Far from all human habitation they lived and toiled alone, intent on amassing so much gold that they need never work again. They deprived themselves of practically everything in order to deny themselves nothing in the future. They were slaves now so that they would be kings later. They were thankful for the isolation: this way there was no chance of others robbing them of their treasure. They had no mind to share with any except their own company. They even stayed away

116

from Santa Fe now that they had so much gold near the camp, thinking that they might be followed sometime and bring trouble on themselves.

Little did they realize that the harm had already been done. A band of men from Santa Fe, reinforced by Indians, were gradually surrounding them, moving up under cover of night and hiding by day. Some of the company had paid in gold when last in Santa Fe and this had started the rumor that they were not just hunting but had found an enormous treasure.

It was about three months after his return that Beale woke up suddenly one night with an acute sense of danger. He reached cautiously for his gun but all was quiet and no one seemed disturbed but himself. All the same he got out of his blankets and went over to the two men who had the night watch. They were quietly talking by the small fire.

"Everything all right?" he asked.

"Quiet as the grave. Why, did you think something was wrong?"

"Must have been a bad dream, I reckon. I woke up smelling trouble."

"Ate too much of that meat. It was darned tough!" said one man. But I'll take another walk around to check out the place. Horses are quiet enough."

"Might as well take a look. It'll help me get back to sleep anyhow. You go one way and I'll go the other."

Beale realized they were humoring him but the feeling of danger persisted. It was a dark night without a moon, otherwise some of the men would have been working. The darkness was like a thick blanket pierced at intervals by the bright flames of the fire. Beale walked toward the far side of the camp. He had picked up a lantern from the men on watch but it gave very little light. The darkness seemed to smother it. There was an uncanny stillness everywhere. It must be just before dawn, he thought, it's always extra dark and quiet then. The night creatures have gone silent and those of the day haven't yet gotten up.

Beale was out of the firelight now walking away from the camp to the place where the gold was hidden. Suddenly his quick ears caught a sound behind him. He whirled round and caught sight of a shadowy figure just as a tremendous blow knocked him unconscious to the ground, his gun exploding as he fell.

When Beale opened his eyes it was daylight. For a moment he could see nothing—the light was too agonizingly bright. His head throbbed with a terrible intensity and it felt as if his scalp was on fire. He put up his hand to feel the wound and encountered a bloody mass of flesh and splintered bone and he knew with a sick horror that he had been scalped. Nausea and pain gripped him and he was slipping back into unconsciousness, but with a tremendous effort of will he pulled his mind back and tried to see what had happened to the camp. He couldn't raise himself up but he rolled over so that he was facing the center. He couldn't believe what he saw. Men lay in the twisted shapes of death, all scalped and horribly mutilated. Vultures were pecking at their flesh. An upturned pot with a few pieces of ore scattered around it told its own tale. The gold was gone!

Rage seized him. Then he realized it didn't matter any more. They who had slaved for it, sacrificed years of their life for it, were gone too. The gold had taken everything, even their lives. There was nothing left of all their toil and sweat. All of it had been for nothing—he was drifting into unconsciousness again when the ugly, naked head of a vulture stared into his face. Desperate, he waved his hands to scare it away, but it moved only a few feet. Did they eat a man alive, Beale wondered feebly? He knew they pecked out a man's eyes first. His throat was so parched he could not make any sound to scare the birds even if he had the strength. His tongue felt a thousand times too big for his mouth. His hands clutched at the earth to relieve the agony of his tortured head. The pain turned his mind and he thought for a moment he was back in Virginia. Then he realized he would never see Virginia again. A sob broke in his throat. Why hadn't they been content with the first batch or even the second lot of gold and silver? They would all be safe at home enjoying it now if they hadn't been so greedy.

The vultures came nearer, causing Beale to flap his hands again. The creatures moved back but one stayed close to him, staring with its cold, hard black eyes. It's waiting for me to die, if I'm still for a second it'll start devouring me. Oh God, put me out of this quickly, he prayed.

But he was a strong man and it took all day to die, a day of agony and horror amid the sound of the vultures tearing into the flesh of his comrades. Beale prayed they were dead, he hoped none was half alive suffering as he did. He hoped whoever had done this to them would suffer worse than himself, but there was none left to bury them decently, none to tell their end to family and friends, none left to bring their murderers to justice.

Oh, for a drink of cool water or some shade from the terrible sun. Beale groaned aloud in his agony and his hands clutched again at the earth. His eyes caught the glitter from the scattered ore. Gold! It was truly an accursed metal. What good was it when the chips were down? It had no value except what a man gave it. It could lie here forever, useless. Only man could use it and if he didn't use it the gold would use him and destroy him. Gold had no goodness, no badness except what men gave it. They had given it nothing, they had simply taken from one piece of land and put it back in another. Beale hoped desperately that Robert Morriss would carry out his instructions. At least someone could use the gold they had hidden and all would not be in vain.

An old saying came into his mind as his clutching hand grew still.

"There's no wealth but life."

13.

When Beale gave the box to Robert Morriss, the latter secreted it with other valuables in his home and did not think any more about it until he received Beale's letter from St. Louis. This he also put with the box and other valuables, fully expecting Beale would return to claim it.

Time passed and no letter containing a key reached Morriss, so he did nothing about opening the box in 1832, but as he grew older he thought he had better open it and try to follow Beale's instructions before it was too late. Accordingly in 1845 he broke the lock and found inside the three codes and two letters. Also inside were several odd bits of paper which seemed meaningless. Morriss was confounded by the responsibility conferred on him, but he was prepared to carry out the promise he had made to Beale.

However, without the key, the ciphers kept their secret. There was nothing Morriss could do. He tried many ways to find the key and spent hours of time which he could not really spare, all to no avail. Then pressure of business and the ill health of his wife prevented him from working on the ciphers for several years. Meanwhile he hoped he would hear from Beale or some other member of the company.

Several times Morriss considered taking a friend into his confidence as the matter weighed on him so heavily. He was a gentle-hearted man and feared that relatives of the men might be in want and he held the means of alleviating their need. But what could he do? If he revealed the matter to a friend wouldn't he be betraying Beale's confidence? On the other hand Beale had told him to entrust it to another if he were sick or near death, but he was neither, so Morriss waited until 1862, when he was 84 years old, before he divulged the secret to his friend James P. Ward.

Even then he was reluctant to tell all of it, but the fear that the secret would die with him and the survivors of Beale's party would be forever deprived of their inheritance, forced him to reveal the whole story.

James Ward was a man much younger than Morriss and Morriss had had opportunity to observe him and to know that he was straightforward and honest. Morriss knew also that Ward was not well off and so would be greatly helped by sharing in the treasure. Morriss made an agreement with Ward that if he would accept the responsibility of the box and its contents, in the event that he deciphered the codes, Ward could take for himself one-half of the share allotted to Morriss and deliver the other half to certain relatives. The remainder of the money was to be held intact for the benefit of those claimants who might be able to authenticate their claims. If, after twenty years, it was still unclaimed, Ward should receive the money for himself and his heirs as a legacy from Morriss.

Ward was very glad to accept the charge entrusted to him and Morriss was relieved of the burden that had weighed upon him for many years. He was now living at the Franklin Hotel, later known as Norvell House, but he moved to the home of a friend where he died in 1865 two years before his wife.

James P. Ward now started upon the labor that was to devour the greater part of his life and happiness. If he had had any idea of the time he would spend, the hours of midnight oil that would be consumed and the amount of money and energy he would spend on the ciphers, he would never have embarked on the thing at all. But he was convinced that careful study soon would yield a quick reward and he was elated with the prospect of such great wealth.

Ward was fascinated and mesmerized by the ciphers; he spent every spare moment he could working on them. At first his wife was interested also, but as time went on and her husband spent more and more time working on them and neglecting her and his family, she began to rebel. But all her complaints had no effect — all he would say was, "I intend to make you wealthy, my dear. Soon we will want for nothing. Just think of what we can do for our children with all that gold."

His wife would be silent for a while and even try to help him as he struggled, first with one method then another.

When Ward first studied the codes he found them unnumbered so for his convenience he numbered them 1, 2 and 3 according to their length. He tried working on each in turn using every document he thought might have been available to Beale at the time he was staying at the hotel in Lynchburg. For years he worked on and on without any success and then one day he began numbering each word of the Declaration of Independence and substituting the first letter of the word corresponding to the numbers in the codes. First he tried code number 1, but it did not work. Then he tried it with code number 2 and to his incredulous astonishment, words began to form. His hands shaking, he wrote on, substituting letters for numbers until he had the following message:

"I have deposited in the County of Bedford about four miles from Buford's in an excavation or vault six feet below the surface of the ground, the following articles belonging jointly to the parties whose names are given in number three herewith.

"The first deposit consisted of ten hundred and fourteen pounds of gold and thirty eight hundred and twelve pounds of silver, deposited Nov eighteen nineteen.

"The second was made Dec eighteen twenty one and consisted of nineteen hundred and seven pounds of gold and twelve hundred and eighty eight of silver; also jewels obtained in St. Louis in exchange to save transportation, and valued at thirteen thousand dollars.

"The above is securely packed in iron pots with iron covers. The vault is roughly lined with stone, and the vessels rest on solid stone, and are covered with others.

"Paper number one describes the exact locality of the vault, so that no difficulty will be had in finding it."

Ward was so overcome when he read the message that he could hardly stand. He had put in so much work for so long without any hope, that it was almost too much for him. His wife came quickly, disturbed by the strange sound of his voice when he called her, and together they went over the message again. They had never thought there would be so much gold and treasure—this was something beyond their wildest dreams. Now they could not wait to start on the others and Mrs. Ward was as eager as her husband. Even their children worked on the codes.

Everything was given up to the codes—work, friends, even health was neglected because they were so sure that soon they would be the possessors of untold wealth.

But alas, the other codes would not yield their secret and after 20 years, discouraged, reduced to poverty and his family separated, Ward decided to put the codes out of his life. He had become addicted to them as surely as any opium eater and he knew that unless he put temptation beyond his reach he would continue to cause suffering to his wife and ruin their happiness. So he resolved to write a pamphlet giving all the details that had been handed to him together with the codes and letters and the secret of the code number 2 which he had deciphered, and make it a public thing.

Ward chose an old friend to act for him in the matter, a man who had known Morriss and who had been named by

124

Morriss as one of the beneficiaries, although he did not know it. They chose Virginia Job Print of Lynchburg to print the pamphlet in 1885, a firm known to them which could be depended on to do the work well. Ward hoped that some poor but honest man would solve the mystery and that whoever was so fortunate would remember the heirs and use the money for some good purpose.

Then having done all this, Ward had second thoughts. Had he the right to give this matter to the public when he might be depriving the rightful heirs of their inheritance? He talked at length with his friend and they could not make up their minds whether it was better to leave the matter unsolved forever or to risk some unscrupulous person finding the treasure and keeping it for himself. In either case the result would be the same and there was the chance that some honorable person would solve the mystery and good would come out of the affair. So they decided to go ahead and sell the pamphlet at 50 cents per copy, which would cover the cost and make a small profit for Ward.

But alas, the ill fortune that had followed Ward throughout all his dealings with the codes dogged him still. That very night a fire broke out in the warehouse and all but a few of the pamphlets were destroyed. These were given to a few friends and were the source of what is known to the people of the Roanoke area of the Beale Treasure.

Ward was a broken man. His son, who was working as a U.S. mail transfer clerk at the union station in Lynchburg, never spent any time on the codes. He had seen what sorrow it brought to his father and mother and never wanted to hear of it again.

So far no one has found the key that Beale left with a friend in St. Louis. It is hoped that someone reading this book might find it among old papers and solve the mystery at last.

Chronology

April 1817	Thomas Jefferson Beale's party set out from Big Lick, Virginia, for the western plains.
May 1817	Party leaves St. Louis for Santa Fe.
December 1817	Party arrives in Santa Fe.
March 1818	Party discovers gold approximately 200 miles north of Santa Fe.
November 1819	Beale makes first deposit of gold and silver near Buford, Virginia.
January 1820	Beale visits Robert Morriss in the Washington Hotel, Lynchburg. He later returns to site where gold is buried.
December 1821	Beale makes second deposit of gold, silver and jewels in Virginia.
January 1822	Beale returns to Washington Hotel, Lynchburg, to see Morriss. He makes ciphers, and writes two letters which he places in an iron box and gives to Robert Morriss for safekeeping.
March 1822	Beale and men leave Virginia for gold camp.
May 1822	Beale sends letter concerning box to Morriss from St. Louis.

127

1845	Morriss opens box and finds three ciphers and two letters.
1862	Morriss gives box containing three ciphers and three letters (including St. Louis letter) to James P. Ward.
1865	Morriss dies.
1884	Ward sends letter regarding copyright to Librarian of Congress.
1885	Ward sends title page of Beale Papers and is granted copyright.
1885	James P. Ward writes pamphlet entitled "The Beale Papers" and gives it to the Virginia Job Print, Lynchburg, Virginia to be published, using an unnamed friend of his and Morriss's as agent.
Late 1885	Fire sweeps through Virginia Job Print and destroys most of the pamphlets before they can be circulated. From the few copies left, various people in the area (including Walter Innis's relatives) obtain copies of the ciphers.
1897	N. Hazlewood of Buford asks Clayton Hart of Roanoke to make copies of ciphers. Hart keeps copies for himself.
1898	Clayton Hart obtains copy of Ward's pamphlet.
1903	Clayton Hart visits Ward and his son, who confirm details in pamphlet.
1919	George Hart Sr. moves to Washington, D.C.
1924	George Hart Sr. sends copy of pamphlet to eminent cryptologist, Col. George Fabyan of Illinois.
February 1925	Col. Fabyan replies, asking for more details.

1931	Jos. McGehee of Roanoke sends typed copy of pamphlet to H.O. Yardley
September 1949	Clayton Hart dies.
January 1952	George Hart writes all he knows and surmises about the Beale Treasure. He gives a copy to the Roanoke Library and sends a copy to Raymond Barnes of Roanoke, who writes several newspaper articles.
1954	Yardley sends codes to Editor of Cryptogram published Dec. 1954.
1962	George Hart gives all his papers to P.B. Innis.
1963	P.B. Innis is given two pieces of paper from box.
August 1964	P.B. Innis publishes article in *Argosy* magazine. Interest in the subject is revived; many clubs start to decipher codes and hunt for treasure.
August 1968	George Hart dies.
April 1972	National Study Committee on Beale Ciphers meets in Washington, D.C.
1973	Book GOLD IN THE BLUE RIDGE by P.B. Innis and Walter D. Innis published by Luce.
Sept 1979	Beale Cypher Symposium, Washington, D.C.
January 1980	P.B. Innis and J. Solario decipher part of code 1.

1982 *Gold in the Blue Ridge* updated. Various persons claim to have deciphered the codes, but no proof or treasure found.

1983 P.B. Innis and C. Cardogan visit Riverbank looking for clues.

1983 P.B. Innis searches Dead Letter boxes for Beale's letter to Mooriss advertised in the *St. Louis Beacon* 1832.

1984 P.B. Innis discovers earlier building than the old chimney.

1988 Walter and P.B. Innis make their 6th dig and find nothing.

1989 Mel Fisher buys land and starts digging for treasure.

1990 P.B. Innis writes article for Treasure Search Magazine stating why Fisher is digging in the wrong place. Many more people digging. No treasure found yet.

1994 *Gold in the Blue Ridge* third edition published.

These papers were prepared by James B. Ward of Campbell County, Virginia, in 1885 and printed in the Virginia Job Print Co. in Lynchburg, Virginia. Unfortunately, all but a very few copies were destroyed by a fire that broke out in the printing plant just before the pamphlets were distributed. They were to sell at 50 cents a copy.

The Beale Papers
by
James B. Ward

The following details of an incident that happened many years ago, but which has lost none of its interest on that account, are now given to the public for the first time.

Until now, for reasons which will be apparent to everyone, all knowledge of this affair was confined to a very limited circle—the writer's immediate family, and to one old and valued friend, upon whose discretion he could always rely. Nor was it ever intended to travel beyond that circle. But circumstances over which he had no control, pecuniary embarrassments of a pressing character, and duty to a dependent family requiring his undivided attention, force him

131

to abandon a task to which he has devoted the best years of his life, but which seems as far from accomplishment as at the start. He is, therefore, compelled, however unwillingly, to relinquish to others the elucidation of the Beale Papers, not doubting that of the many who will give the subject attention, some one, through fortune or accident, will speedily solve their mystery and secure the prize which has eluded him.

It can be readily imagined that this course was not determined upon all at once. Regardless of the entreaties of his family and the persistent advice of his friends, who were formerly as sanguine as himself, he stubbornly continued his investigations, until absolute want stared him in the face and forced him to yield to their persuasions. Having now lost all hope of benefit from this source to himself, he is not unwilling that others may receive it, and only hopes that the prize may fall to some poor, but honest man, who will use his discovery not solely for the promotion of his own enjoyment, but for the welfare of others.

Until the writer lost all hope of ultimate success, he toiled faithfully at his work. Unlike any other pursuit with practical and natural results, a charm attended it, independent of the ultimate benefit he expected; and the possibility of success lent an interest and excitement to the work not to be resisted.

It would be difficult to portray the delight he experienced when accident revealed to him the explanation of paper marked "No. 2". Unmeaning, as this had hitherto been, it was now fully explained, and no difficulty was apprehended in mastering the others. But this accident, affording so much pleasure at the time, was a most unfortunate one for him, as it induced him to neglect family, friends, and all legitimate pursuits for what has proved, so far, the veriest illusion.

It will be seen by a perusal of Mr. Beale's letter to Mr.

132

Morriss that he promised, under certain contingencies, such as failure to see or communicate with him in a given time, to furnish a key by which the papers would be fully explained.

As the failure to do either actually occurred, and the promised explanation has never been received, it may possibly remain in the hands of some relative or friend of Beale's, or some other person engaged in the enterprise with him. That they would attach no importance to a seemingly unintelligible writing seems quite natural; but their attention being called to them by the publication of this narrative, may result in eventually bringing to light the missing papers.

Mr. Beale, who deposited with Mr. Morriss the papers which form the subject of this history, is described as being a gentleman well educated, evidently of good family, and with popular manners. What motives could have influenced him and so many others to risk their health and their lives in such an undertaking, except the natural love of daring adventure, with its consequent excitement, we can only conjecture.

We may suppose, and indeed we have his word for so doing, that they were infatuated with the dangers, and with the wild and roving character of their lives, the charms of which lured them farther and farther from civilization, until their lives were sacrificed to their temerity. This was the opinion of Mr. Morriss, and in this way only can we account for the fact that the treasure for which they sacrificed so much, constituting almost fabulous wealth, lies abandoned and unclaimed for more than half a century.

Should any of my readers be more fortunate than myself in discovering its place of concealment, I shall not only rejoice with them, but feel that I have at least accomplished something in contributing to the happiness of others.

The Late Robert Morriss.

Robert Morriss, the custodian of the Beale Papers, was

born in 1778 in the State of Maryland, but removed at an early age, with his family, to Loudoun County, Virginia, where, in 1803, he married Miss Sarah Mitchell, a fine looking and accomplished young lady of that county.

In obtaining such a wife Mr. Morriss was peculiarly fortunate, as her subsequent career fully demonstrated. As a wife she was without reproach, as a generous and sympathizing woman she was without an equal—the poor will long remember her charities, and lament the friend they have lost.

Shortly after his removal to Lynchburg Mr. Morriss engaged in the mercantile business, and shortly thereafter he became a purchaser and shipper of tobacco to an extent hitherto unknown in this section. In these pursuits he was eminently successful for several years, and speedily accumulated a comfortable independence.

It was during this period of his success that Mr. Morriss erected the first brick building of which the town could boast, and which still stands on Main Street, a monument to his enterprise. His private residence, the house now owned and occupied by Max Guggenheimer, Esquire, at the head of Main Street, I think he also built. There the most unbounded hospitality reigned, and every facility for enjoyment was furnished. The elite of the town assembled there more frequently than elsewhere, and there are now living some whose pleasant recollections are associated with that period.

The happiness of Mr. Morriss, however, was of short duration, for reverses came when they were least expected. Heavy purchases of tobacco, at ruinous figures, in anticipation of an upward market, which visions were never realized, swept from him in a moment the savings of years, and left him nothing save his honor and the sincere sympathy of the community, with which to begin the battle anew.

It was at this time that Mrs. Morriss exhibited the loveliest traits of her character. Seemingly unmindful of her con-

134

dition, with a smiling face and cheering words, she so encouraged her husband that he became almost reconciled to his fate.

Thrown thus upon his own resources, by the advice of his wife, Mr. Morriss leased for a term of years the Washington Hotel, known now as the Arlington, on Church Street, and commenced the business of hotel keeping. His kind disposition, strict probity, excellent management, and well-ordered household, soon rendered him famous as a host, and his reputation extended even to other States. His was the house par excellence of the town, and no fashionable assemblages met at any other.

Finding, in a few years, that his experiment was successful and his business remunerative, he removed to the Franklin Hotel, now the Norvell House, the largest and best arranged in the city. This house he conducted for many years, enjoying the friendship and countenance of the first men of the country. Amongst his guests and devoted friends were Jackson, Clay, Coles, Witcher, Chief Justice Marshall, and a host of others scarcely less distinguished might be enumerated.

But it was not the wealthy and distinguished alone who appreciated Mr. Morriss. The poor and lowly had blessings for the man who sympathized with their misfortunes, and was ever ready to relieve their distress. Many poor but worthy families, whose descendants are now in our midst, can remember the fact that his table supplied their daily food, not for days and weeks only, but for months at a time. And, as a further instance of his forbearance and unparalleled generosity, there are now living those who will testify to the fact that he permitted a boarder, in no way connected with him, to remain in his house for more than twenty years, and until he died, without ever receiving the slightest remuneration, and that he was never made to feel otherwise than as a favored guest.

In manner Mr. Morriss was courteous and gentle; but when occasion demanded he could be stern and determined, too. He was emphatically the master of his house, and from his decision there was no appeal. As an "old Virginia gentleman", he was sans peur et sans reproche, *and to a remarkable extent, possessed the confidence and affection of his friends.*

After a checquered and eventful life of more than eighty years, passed mostly in business, which brought him in contact with all classes of people, he died, lamented by all, and leaving not an enemy behind. His death, which occurred in 1863, was just two years subsequent to that of his wife. It can be truly said that no persons ever lived in a community for such a length of time who accomplished more good during their lives, or whose death was more universally regretted.

It was the unblemished character of the man, and the universal confidence reposed in him, that induced Beale to entrust him with his secret, and, in certain contingencies, select him for a most important post. That his confidence was not misplaced every one remembering Mr. Morriss will acknowledge.

It was in 1862, the second year of the Confederate war, that Mr. Morriss first intimated the possession of a secret that was destined to make some persons wealthy. At first he was not very communicative, nor did I press him to reveal what he seemed to speak of with reluctance. In a few weeks, however, his mind seemed changed, and he voluntarily proffered his confidence.

Inviting me to his room, with no one to interrupt us, he gave me an outline of the matter, which soon enlisted my interest and created an intense longing to learn more. About this time, however, affairs of importance required my presence in Richmond, and prevented further communication between us until after my return, when I found Mr. Morriss ready to resume the interesting subject. A private interview was soon arranged, and, after several preliminaries had been complied with, the papers upon which this history is based were delivered into my possession.

The reasons which influenced Mr. Morriss in selecting me for the trust he gave, and were, in substance, as follows: First, friendship for myself and family, whom he would benefit if he could. Second, the knowledge that I was young and in circumstances to afford leisure for the task imposed. And, finally, a confidence that I would regard his instructions and carry out his wishes regarding his charge. These, and perhaps others, he gave during our frequent conversations upon the subject; and, doubtless, he believed he was conferring a favor which would redound greatly to my advantage. That it has proved otherwise is a misfortune to me, but no fault of his.

The conditions alluded to above were that I should devote as much time as was practicable to the papers he had given me; master, if possible, their contents, and if successful in deciphering their meaning and eventually finding the treasure, to appropriate one-half of his portion as a remuneration for my services, the other half to be distributed to certain relatives and connexions of his own, whose names he gave me; the remainder to be held by me in trust for the benefit of such claimants as might at any time appear and be able to authenticate their claims. This latter amount to be left intact subject to such demands for the space of twenty years, when, if still unclaimed, it should revert to myself or my heirs, as a legacy from himself.

As there was nothing objectionable in this, the required promise was given, and the box and contents were placed in my possession.

When the writer recalls his anxious hours, his midnight vigils, his toil, his hopes and disappointments, all consequent upon this promise, he can only conclude that the legacy of Mr. Morriss was not as he designed it—a blessing in disguise.

Having assumed the responsibilities and consented to the requirements of Mr. Morriss, I determined to devote as much time to the accomplishment of the task as could be consistently spared from other duties. With this purpose in view I requested from Mr. Morriss a statement of every particular connected with the affair or having the slightest bearing upon it, together with such views and opinions of his own as might ultimately benefit me in my researches. In reply he gave me the following, which I reduced to writing and filed with the papers for future reference:

"It was in the month of January, 1820, while keeping the Washington Hotel, that I first saw and became acquainted with Beale. In company with two others he came to my house seeking entertainment for himself and friends. Being assured of a comfortable provision for themselves and their horses, Beale stated his intention of remaining for the winter, should nothing occur to alter his plans, but that the gentlemen accompanying him would leave in a few days for Richmond, near which place they resided; and that they were anxious to reach their homes, from which they had long been absent.

"They all appeared to be gentlemen, and with a free and independent air, which rendered them peculiarly attractive. After remaining a week or ten days the two left, with expressions of satisfaction with their visit. Beale, who remained, soon became a favored and popular guest. His social disposition and friendly demeanor rendered him extremely popular with every one, particularly the ladies, and a pleasant and friendly intercourse was quickly established between them.

"In person Beale was about six feet in height, with jet black eyes, and hair of the same color, worn longer than was the style at that time. His form was symmetrical and gave evidence of unusual strength and activity. But his distinguishing feature was a dark and swarthy complexion, as if

138

much exposure to the sun and weather had thoroughly tanned and discolored him.

"This, however, did not detract from his appearance; and I thought him the handsomest man I had ever seen. Altogether, he was a model of manly beauty, favored by the ladies and envied by the men. To the first he was reverentially tender and polite; to the latter, affable and courteous when they kept within bounds, but, if they were supercilious or presuming, the lion was aroused, and woe to the man who offended him. Instances of that character occurred more than once while he was my guest, and always resulted in his demanding and receiving an apology. His character soon became universally known, and he was no longer troubled by impertinence.

"Such a man was Thomas Jefferson Beale, as he appeared in 1820, and in his subsequent visits to my house. He registered simply from Virginia, but I am of the impression he was from some western portion of the State. Curiously enough, he never adverted to his family or to his antecedents, nor did I question him concerning them, as I would have done had I dreamed of the interest that in the future would attach to his name.

"Mr. Beale remained with me until about the latter end of the following March, when he left, with the same friends who first accompanied him to my house and who had returned some days before.

"After this I heard nothing from Mr. Beale until January, 1822, when he once more made his appearance, the same genial and popular gentleman as before, but, if possible, darker and swarthier than ever. His welcome was a genuine one, as all were delighted to see him.

"In the Spring, at about the same time, he again left. But, before doing so, Beale handed to me this box, which, as he said, contained papers of value and importance, and which he desired to leave in my charge until called for hereafter. Of course, I did not decline to receive them, but little imagined their importance until his letter from St. Louis was received. This letter I carefully preserved, and it will be given with these papers.

"The box was of iron, carefully locked, and of such weight as to render it a safe depository for articles of value. I placed it in a safe and secure place, where it could not be disturbed until such time as it should be demanded by its owner.

"The letter I alluded to above was the last communication I ever received from Beale, and I never saw him again. I can only suppose that he was killed by Indians, afar from his home, though nothing was heard of his death. His companions, too, must all have shared his fate as no one has ever demanded the box or claimed his effects.

"The box was left in my hands in the Spring of 1822, and, by authority of his letter, I should have examined its contents in 1832, ten years thereafter, having heard nothing from Beale in the meantime. But it was not until 1845, some 23 years after it came into my possession, that I decided upon opening it. During that year I had the lock broken, and, with the exception of the two letters to myself, and some old receipts, found only some unintelligible papers, covered with figures, and totally incomprehensible to me.

"According to his letter these papers convey all the information necessary to find the treasure he has concealed, and upon you devolves the responsibility of recovering it. Should you succeed you will be amply reimbursed for your work, and others near and dear to me will likewise be benefited. The end is worth all your exertions, and I have every hope that success will reward your efforts."

Such, in substance, was the statement of Mr. Morriss in answer to the various interrogatories propounded to him. And, finding that I could elicit no further information, I resolved to do the best I could with the limited means at my disposal.

I commenced by reading over and over again the letters to Mr. Morriss, endeavoring to impress each syllable they contained on my memory, and to extract from them, if possible, some meaning or allusion that might give, perhaps, a faint or barely perceptible hint as a guide. No such clew, however, could I find, and where or how to commence was a problem I found most difficult to solve.

To systematize a plan for my work I arranged the papers in the order of their length, and numbered them, designing to commence with the first and devote my whole attention to that until I had either unraveled its meaning or was convinced of its impossibility—afterwards to take up the others, and proceed as before.

All of this I did in the course of time, but failed so completely that my hopes of solving the mystery were well nigh abandoned. My thoughts, however, were constantly upon it, and the figures contained in each paper, in their regular order, were fixed in my memory. My impression was that each figure represented a letter, but as the numbers so greatly exceeded the letters of the alphabet, I wondered if it were possible that some document had been used, and the words numbered.

With this idea in mind a test was made of every book I could produce, by numbering the letters and comparing their numbers with those of the manuscript. All to no purpose, however, until the Declaration of Independence afforded the clew to one of the papers, and revived all my hopes.

To enable my readers to better understand the explanation of this paper the Declaration of Independence is given here with the words numbered in consecutive order. I am sure this will be of interest to those designing to follow up my investigations.

When I first made this discovery I thought I had the key

to the whole, but soon ascertained that further work was necessary before my task could be completed. The encouragement afforded, however, by this discovery enabled me to proceed, and I have persisted in my labors to the present time. Now, as I have already said, I am forced by circumstances to devote my time to other pursuits, and to abandon hopes which were destined never to be realized.

The following is the letter addressed to Mr. Morriss by Beale and dated St. Louis, May, 1822, and was the latest communication ever received from him:

St. Louis, Mo., May 9, 1822.

Robt. Morriss, Esq.,

My esteemed friend:

Ever since leaving my comfortable quarters at your house I have been journeying to this place, and only succeeded in reaching it yesterday. I have had, altogether, a pleasant time, the weather being fine and the atmosphere bracing. I shall remain here a week or ten days longer, then "ho" for the plains, to hunt buffalo and encounter the savage grizzlies. How long I may be absent I cannot now determine, certainly not less than two years, perhaps longer.

With regard to the box left in your charge I have a few words to say, and, if you will permit me, give you some instructions concerning it. It contains papers vitally affecting the fortunes of myself and many others engaged in business with me, and in the event of my death its loss might be irreparable. You will, therefore, see the necessity of guarding it with vigilance and care to prevent so great a catastrophe. It also contains some letters addressed to yourself and which will be necessary to enlighten you concerning the business in which we are engaged.

Should none of us ever return you will please preserve carefully the box for a period of ten years from the date of *this letter, and if I, or no one with authority from me, during that time demands its restoration, you will open it, which can be done by removing the lock.*

You will find, in addition to the papers addressed to you, other papers which will be unintelligible without the aid of a key to assist you. Such a key I have left in the hands of a friend in this place, sealed, addressed to yourself, and endorsed "Not to be delivered until June, 1832". By means of this you will understand fully all you will be required to do.

I know you will cheerfully comply with this request, thus adding to the many obligations under which you have already placed me. In the meantime should death or sickness happen to you, to which all are liable, please select from among your friends some one worthy, and to him hand this letter, and to him delegate your authority.

I have been thus particular in my instructions in consequence of the somewhat perilous enterprise in which we are engaged, but trust we shall meet long ere the time expires, and so save you this trouble. Be the result what it may, however, the game is worth the candle and we will play it to the end.

With kindest wishes for your most excellent wife, compliments to the ladies, a good word to enquiring friends, if there be any, and assurances of my highest esteem for yourself, I remain, as ever,

Your sincere friend,

Tho^S. Jeff^n. Beale.

After the reception of this letter Mr. Morriss states that he was particularly careful to see the box securely placed, where it could remain in absolute safety so long as the exigencies of the case might require. The letter, too, he was equally careful to preserve for future use should it be needed.

Having done all that was required of him, Mr. Morriss could only await Beale's return, or some communication from him. In either case he was disappointed, nor did a line or message ever reach him.

During this period rumors of Indian outrages and massacres were current, but no mention of Beale's name ever occurred. What became of him and his companions is left entirely to conjecture. Whether he was slain by Indians, or killed by the savage animals of the Rocky Mountains, or whether exposure, and perhaps privation, did its work can never be told. One thing at least is certain, that of the young and gallant band, whose buoyant spirits led them to seek such a life and to forsake the comforts of home, with all its enjoyments, for the dangers and privations they must necessarily encounter, not a survivor remains.

Though Mr. Morriss was aware of the contents of the box in 1845 it was not until 1862, forty years after he received it, that he thought proper to mention its existence, and to myself alone did he then divulge it. He had become long since satisfied that the parties were no longer living, but his delicacy of feeling prevented him assuming as a fact a matter so pregnant with consequences. He frequently decided upon doing so, and as often delayed it for another time. And when, at last, he did speak of the matter it was with seeming reluctance, as if he felt he was committing a wrong. But the story once told he evinced up to the time of his death the greatest interest in my success, and in frequent interviews encouraged me to proceed.

It is now more than twenty years since these papers came into my hands, and, with the exception of one of them, they are still as incomprehensible as ever. Much time was devoted to this one, and those who engage in the matter will be saved what has been consumed upon it myself.

Before giving the papers to the public I would say a

word to those who may take an interest in them, and give them a little advice, acquired by bitter experience. It is, to devote only such time as can be spared from your legitimate business to the task, and, if you can spare no time, let the matter alone. Should you disregard my advice, do not hold me responsible that poverty you have courted is more easily found than the accomplishment of your wishes, and I would avoid the sight of another reduced to my condition.

Nor is it necessary to devote the time that I did to this matter, as accident alone, without the promised key, will ever develop the mystery. If revealed by accident a few hours devoted to the subject may accomplish results which were denied to years of patient toil. Again, never, as I have done, sacrifice your own and your family's interests to what may prove an illusion. But, as I have already said, when your day's work is done, and you are comfortably seated by your good fire, a short time devoted to the subject can injure no one, and may bring its reward.

By pursuing this policy your interests will not suffer, your family will be cared for, and your thoughts will not be absorbed to the exclusion of other important matters. With this admonition I submit to my readers the papers upon which this narrative is founded.

The first, in order, is the letter from Beale to Mr. Morriss, which will give the reader a clearer conception of all the facts connected with the case, and enable him to understand as fully as I myself do the present status of the affair. The letter is as follows:

Lynchburg, Va., January 4th, 1822.
My dear friend Morriss:

You will, doubtless, be surprised when you discover, from a perusal of this letter, the importance of the trust confided to you, and the confidence reposed in your honor, by parties whom you have never seen and whose names you have never heard. The reasons are simple and easily told: It was imperative upon us that some one here should be selected to carry out our wishes in case of accident to ourselves, and your reputation as a man of integrity, unblemished honor, and business sagacity, influenced them to select you in place of others better known but, perhaps, not so reliable as yourself.

It was with this design that I first visited your house, two years since, that I might judge by personal observation if your reputation was merited. To enable me the better to do so I remained with you more than three months, and until I was fully satisfied as to your character. This visit was made by the request of my associates, and you can judge from their actions whether my report was a favorable one.

I will now give you some idea of the enterprise in which we are engaged, and the duties which will be required of you in connection therewith; first assuring you, however, that your compensation for the trouble will be ample, as you have been unanimously made one of our association, and as such are entitled to share equally with the others.

Some five years since I, in connection with several friends, who, like myself, were fond of adventure, and if mixed with a little danger all the more acceptable, determined to visit the great Western plains and enjoy in hunting buffalo, grizzly bears, and such other game as the country would afford. This, at that time, was our sole object, and we at once proceeded to put it in execution.

On account of Indians and other dangers incident to such an undertaking, we determined to raise a party of not less than thirty individuals, of good character and standing, who would be pleasant companions and financially able to encounter the expense. With this object in view each one of us suggested the subject to his several friends and acquaintances, and in a few weeks the requisite number had signed the conditions and were admitted as members of the party. Some few refused to join us, being, doubtless, deterred by the dangers, but such men we did not want, and were glad of their refusal.

The company being formed, we forthwith commenced our preparations, and, early in April, 1817, left old Virginia for St. Louis, Mo., where we expected to purchase the necessary outfits, procure a guide and two or three servants; and obtain such information and advice as might be beneficial hereafter. All was done as intended, and we left St. Louis the 19th of May; to be absent two years, our objective point being Santa Fe, which we intended to reach in the ensuing Fall, and there establish ourselves in winter quarters.

After leaving St. Louis we were advised by our guide to form a regular military organization, with a captain, to be selected by the members, to whom should be given sole authority to manage our affairs, and, in case of necessity, ensure united action. This was agreed to, and each member of the party bound himmelf by a solemn obligation to obey, at all times, the orders of their captain, or, in event of refusal, to leave the company at once.

This arrangement was to remain in force for two years, or for the period of our expected absence. Tyranny, partiality, incompetence, or other improper conduct on the part of the captain was to be punished by deposing him from his office if a majority of the company desired his dismissal. All this being arranged, and a set of laws framed, by which the conduct of the members was to be regulated, the election was held, and resulted in choosing me as their leader.

It is not my purpose now to give you details of our wanderings, or of the pleasures or dangers encountered. All this I will reserve until we meet again, when it will be a pleasure to recall incidents that will always be fresh in my memory.

About the first of December we reached our destination,

Santa Fe, and prepared for a long and welcome rest from the fatigues of our journey. Nothing of interest occurred during the winter, and of this little Mexican town we soon became heartily tired. We longed for the advent of weather which would enable us to resume our wanderings and our exhilarating pursuits.

Early in March some of the party, to vary the monotony of their lives, determined upon a short excursion, for the purpose of hunting and examining the country around us. They expected to be only a few days absent, but days passed into weeks, and weeks into a month or more, before we had any tidings of the party.

We had become exceedingly uneasy and were preparing to send out scouts to trace them, if possible, when two of the party arrived and gave an explanation of their absence. It appears that when they left Santa Fe they pursued a northerly course for some days, being successful in finding an abundance of game, which they secured, and were on the eve of returning when they discovered on their left an immense herd of buffaloes heading for a valley just perceptible in the distance. They determined to follow them, and secure as many as possible. Keeping well together they followed their trail for two weeks or more, securing many, and stampeding the rest.

One day, while following them, the party encamped in a small ravine, some 250 or 300 miles to the north of Santa Fe, and, with their horses tethered, were preparing their evening meal when one of the men discovered in a cleft of the rocks something that had the appearance of gold. Upon showing it to the others it was pronounced to be gold—and much excitement was the natural consequence. Messengers were at once dispatched to inform me of the facts and request my presence with the rest of the party—and with supplies for an indefinite time.

148

All the pleasures and temptations which had lured them to the plains were now forgotten, and visions of boundless wealth and future grandeur were the only ideas entertained.

Upon reaching the locality I found all as it had been represented, and the excitement intense. Every one was diligently at work with such tools and appliances as they had improvised, and quite a little pile had already accumulated. Though all were at work there was nothing like order or method in their plans, and my first efforts were to systematize our operations and reduce everything to order.

With this object in view an agreement was entered into to work in common, as joint partners, the accumulations of each one to be placed in a common receptacle, and each be entitled to an equal share of the whole whenever he chose to withdraw it; the whole to remain under my charge until some other disposition of it was agreed upon.

Under this arrangement the work progressed favorably for eighteen months or more, and a great deal of gold had accumulated in my hands, as well as silver, which had likewise been found. Everything necessary for our purposes and for the prosecution of the work had been obtained from Santa Fe, and no trouble was experienced in procuring assistance from the Indians in our labors.

Matters went on thus until the Summer of 1819, when the question of transferring our wealth to some secure place was frequently discussed. It was not considered advisable to retain so large an amount in so wild and dangerous a locality, where its very possession might endanger our lives; and to conceal it there would avail nothing, as we might at any time be forced to reveal its place of concealment.

We were in a dilemma. Some advised one plan, some another. One recommended Santa Fe as the safest place to deposit it, while others objected and advocated its shipment at once to the States, where it was ultimately to go, and where alone it would be safe. The idea seemed to prevail, and it was doubtless correct, that when outside parties ascertained, as they would do, that we kept nothing on hand to tempt their cupidity, our lives would be more secure than at present.

It was finally decided that it would be best to send it to Virginia, under my charge, and there be securely buried in a cave near Buford's Tavern, in the county of Bedford, which all of us had visited, and which was considered a perfectly safe depository. This was acceptable to all, and I at once made preparations for my departure. The whole party were to accompany me for the first five hundred miles, when all but ten would return, these latter to remain with me to the end of the journey. All was carried out as arranged, and I arrived safely with my charge.

Stopping at Buford's Tavern, where we remained for a month, under pretense of hunting, etc., we visited the cave but found it unfit for our purpose. It was too frequently visited by the neighboring farmers, who used it as a receptacle for their sweet potatoes and other vegetables. We soon selected a better place, and to this the treasure was safely transferred.

Before leaving my companions on the plains it was suggested that, in case of an accident to ourselves, the treasure so concealed would be lost to their relatives without some provision against such a contingency. I was, therefore, instructed to select some perfectly reliable person, if such an one could be found, who should, in the event of his proving acceptable to the party, be confided in to carry out their wishes in regard to their respective shares, and upon my return report whether I had found such a person. It was in accordance with these instructions that I visited you, made your acquaintance, was satisfied that you would suit us, and so reported.

On my return I found the work still progressing

favorably, and, by making large accessions to our force of laborers, I was ready to return last Fall with an increased supply of metal, which came through safely and was deposited with the other. It was at this time I handed you the box, not disclosing the nature of its contents but asking you to keep it safely till called for. I intend writing you, however, from St. Louis, and impress upon you its importance still more forcibly.

The papers enclosed herewith will be unintelligible without the key, which will reach you in time, and will be found merely to state the contents of our depository, with its exact location, and a list of the names of our party, with their places of residence, etc.

I thought, at first, to give you their names in this letter, but reflecting that some one may read the letter, and thus be enabled to impose upon you by personating some member of the party, have decided the present plan is best.

You will be aware from what I have written that we are engaged in a perilous enterprise; one which promises glorious results if successful, but dangers intervene, and of the end no one can tell. We can only hope for the best, and persevere until our work is accomplished, and the sum secured for which we are striving.

As ten years must elapse before you will see this letter, you may well conclude by that time that the worst has happened, and that none of us is to be numbered with the living. In such an event you will please visit the place of deposit and secure its contents, which you will divide into thirty-one equal parts. One of these parts you are to retain as your own, freely given you for your services. The other shares to be distributed to the parties named in the accompanying paper. These legacies, so unexpectedly received, will at least serve to recall names that may still be cherished though partially forgotten.

In conclusion, my dear friend, I beg that you will not

allow any false or idle punctillio to prevent your receiving and appropriating the portion assigned to yourself. It is a gift, not from myself alone but from each member of our party, and will not be out of proportion to the services required of you.

I trust, my dear Mr. Morriss, that we may meet many times in the future, but if the Fates forbid, with my last communication I would assure you of the entire respect and confidence of

Your friend,

Tho^S. Jeffⁿ. Beale

The second letter in the box is as follows:

Lynchburg, Va., January 5th, 1822.

Dear Mr. Morriss:

You will find in one of the papers, written in cipher, the names of all my associates, and opposite to the name of each one will be found the names and residences of relatives and others, to whom they devise their respective portions.

From this you will be enabled to carry out the wishes of all by distributing the portion of each to the parties designated. This will not be difficult as their residences are given, and they can easily be found.

T.J.B.

The two letters given above were all the box contained that were intelligible. The others consisted of papers closely covered with figures, which were, of course, unmeaning until they could be deciphered. To do this was the task to which I now devoted myself, and with but partial success; that is, as to deciphering paper marked "No. 2", to be described later on.

The three ciphers are given below, the one marked "No. 1" describing the exact locality of the vault where the treasure is buried; the one marked "No. 2" stating the contents of the vault; and paper marked "No. 3" stating the names and addresses of the persons involved:

No. 1.

71, 194, 38, 1701, 89, 76, 11, 83, 1629, 48, 94, 63, 132, 16, 111, 95, 84, 341, 975, 14, 40, 64, 27, 81, 139, 213, 63, 90, 1120, 8, 15, 3, 126, 2018, 40, 74, 758, 485, 604, 230, 436, 664, 582, 150, 251, 284, 308, 231, 124, 211, 486, 225, 401, 370, 11, 101, 305, 139, 189, 17, 33, 88, 208, 193, 145, 1, 94, 73, 416, 918, 263, 28, 500, 538, 356, 117, 136, 219, 27, 176, 130, 10, 460, 25, 485, 18, 436, 65, 84, 200, 283, 118, 320, 138, 36, 416, 280 15, 71, 224, 961, 44, 16, 401, 39, 88, 61, 304, 12, 21, 24, 283, 134, 92, 63, 246, 486, 682, 7, 219, 184, 360, 780, 18, 64, 463, 474, 131, 160, 79, 73, 440, 95, 18, 64, 581, 34, 69, 128, 367, 460, 17, 81, 12, 103, 820, 62, 116, 97, 103, 862, 70, 60, 1317, 471, 540, 208, 121, 890, 346, 36, 150, 59, 568, 614, 13, 120, 63, 219, 812, 2160, 1780, 99, 35, 18, 21, 136, 872, 15, 28, 170, 88, 4, 30, 44, 112, 18, 147, 436, 195, 320, 37, 122, 113, 6, 140, 8, 120, 305, 42, 58, 461, 44, 106, 301, 13, 408, 680, 93, 86, 116, 530, 82, 568, 9, 102, 38, 416, 89, 71, 216, 728, 965, 818, 2, 38, 121, 195, 14, 326, 148, 234, 18, 55, 131, 234, 361, 824, 5, 81, 623, 48, 961, 19, 26, 33, 10, 1101, 365, 92, 88, 181, 275, 346, 201, 206, 86, 36, 219, 320, 829, 840, 68, 326, 19, 48, 122, 85, 216, 284, 919, 861, 326, 985, 233, 64, 68, 232, 431, 960, 50, 29, 81, 216, 321, 603, 14, 612, 81, 360, 36, 51, 62, 194, 78, 60, 200, 314, 676, 112, 4, 28, 18, 61, 136, 247, 819, 921, 1060, 464, 895, 10, 6,

153

66, 119, 38, 41, 49, 602, 423, 962, 302, 294, 875,
78, 14, 23, 111, 109, 62, 31, 501, 823, 216, 280, 34,
24, 150, 1000, 162, 286, 19, 21, 17, 340, 19, 242,
31, 86, 234, 140, 607, 115, 33, 191, 67, 104, 86, 52,
88, 16, 80, 121, 67, 95, 122, 216, 548, 96, 11, 201,
77, 364, 218, 65, 667, 890, 236, 154, 211, 10, 98,
34, 119, 56, 216, 119, 71, 218, 1164, 1496, 1817, 51,
39, 210, 36, 3, 19, 540, 232, 22, 141, 617, 84, 290,
80, 46, 207, 411, 150, 29, 38, 46, 172, 85, 194, 36,
261, 543, 897, 624, 18, 212, 416, 127, 931, 19, 4, 63,
96, 12, 101, 418, 16, 140, 230, 460, 538, 19, 27,
88, 612, 1431, 90, 716, 275, 74, 83, 11, 426, 89,
72, ·84, 1300, 1706, 814, 221, 132, 40, 102, 34, 858,
975, 1101, 84, 16, 79, 23, 16, 81, 122, 324, 403, 912,
227, 936, 447, 55, 86, 34, 43, 212, 107, 96, 314, 264,
1065, 323, 428, 601, 203, 124, 95, 216, 814, 2906,
654, 820, 2, 301, 112, 176, 213, 71, 87, 96, 202, 35,
10, 2, 41, 17, 84, 221, 736, 820, 214, 11, 60, 760.

-----oOo-----

No. 2.

115, 73, 24, 818, 37, 52, 49, 17, 31, 62, 657,
22, 7, 15, 140, 47, 29, 107, 79, 84, 56, 238, 10, 26,
822, 5, 195, 308, 85, 52, 159, 136, 59, 210, 36, 9,
46, 316, 543, 122, 106, 95, 53, 58, 2, 42, 7, 35, 122,
53, 31, 82, 77, 250, 195, 56, 96, 118, 71, 140, 287,
28, 353, 37, 994, 65, 147, 818, 24, 3, 8, 12, 47, 43,
59, 818, 45, 316, 101, 41, 78, 154, 994, 122, 138, 190,
16, 77, 49, 102, 57, 72, 34, 73, 85, 35, 371, 59, 195,
81, 92, 190, 106, 273, 60, 394, 629 ,270, 219, 106,
388, 287, 63, 3, 6, 190, 122, 43, 233, 400, 106, 290,
314, 47, 48, 81, 96, 26, 115, 92, 157, 190, 110, 77,
85, 196, 46, 10, 113, 140, 353, 48, 120, 106, 2, 616,

61, 420, 822, 29, 125, 14, 20, 37, 105, 28, 248, 16,
158, 7, 35, 19, 301, 125, 110, 496, 287, 98, 117, 520,
62, 51, 219, 37, 113, 140, 818, 138, 549, 8, 44, 287,
388, 117, 18, 79, 344, 34, 20, 59, 520, 557, 107, 612,
219, 37, 66, 154, 41, 20, 50, 6, 584, 122, 154, 248,
110, 61, 52, 33, 30, 5, 38, 8, 14, 84, 57, 549, 216,
115, 71, 29, 85, 63, 43, 131, 29, 138, 47, 73, 238,
549, 52, 53, 79, 118, 51, 44, 63, 195, 12, 238, 112,
3, 49, 79, 353, 105, 56, 371, 566, 210, 515, 125, 360,
133, 143, 101, 15, 284, 549, 252, 14, 204, 140, 344,
26, 822, 138, 115, 48, 73, 34, 204, 316, 616, 63, 219,
7, 52, 150, 44, 52, 16, 40, 37, 157, 818, 37, 121, 12,
95, 10, 15, 35, 12, 131, 62, 115, 102, 818, 49, 53,
135, 138, 30, 31, 62, 67, 41, 85, 63, 10, 106, 818,
138, 8, 113, 20, 32, 33, 37, 353, 287, 140, 47, 85,
50, 37, 49, 47, 64, 6, 7, 71, 33, 4, 43, 47, 63, 1,
27, 609, 207, 229, 15, 190, 246, 85, 94, 520, 2, 270,
20, 39, 7, 33, 44, 22, 40, 7, 10, 3, 822, 106, 44,
496, 229, 353, 210, 199, 31, 10, 38, 140, 297, 61,
612, 320, 302, 676, 287, 2, 44, 33, 32, 520, 557,
10, 6, 250, 566, 246, 53, 37, 52, 83, 47, 320, 38,
33, 818, 7, 44, 30, 31, 250, 10, 15, 35, 106, 159,
113, 31, 102, 406, 229, 549, 320, 29, 66, 33, 101,
818, 138, 301, 316, 353, 320, 219, 37, 52, 28, 549,
320, 33, 8, 48, 107, 50, 822, 7, 2, 113, 73, 16. 125,
11, 110, 67, 102, 818, 33, 59, 81, 157, 38, 43, 590,
138, 19, 85, 400, 38, 43, 77, 14, 27, 8, 47, 138, 63,
140, 44, 35, 22, 176, 106, 250, 314, 216, 2, 10, 7,
994, 4, 20, 25, 44, 48, 7, 26, 46, 110, 229, 818, 190,
34, 112, 147, 44, 110, 121, 125, 96, 41, 51, 50, 140,
56, 47, 152, 549, 63, 818, 28, 42, 250, 138, 591, 98,
653, 32, 107, 140, 112, 26, 85, 138, 549, 50, 20, 125,
371, 38, 36, 10, 52, 118, 136, 102, 420, 150, 112,
71, 14, 20, 7, 24, 18, 12, 818, 37, 67, 110, 62, 33,

155

21, 95, 219, 520, 102, 822, 30, 83, 84, 305, 629, 15,
2, 10, 8, 219, 106, 353, 105, 106, 60, 242, 72, 8, 50,
204, 184, 112, 125, 549, 65, 106, 818, 190, 96, 110,
16, 73, 33, 818, 150, 409, 400, 50, 154, 285, 96, 106,
316, 270, 204, 101, 822, 400, 8, 44, 37, 52, 40, 240,
34, 204, 38, 16, 46, 47, 85, 24, 44, 15, 64, 73, 138,
818, 85, 78, 110, 33, 420, 515, 53, 37, 38, 22, 31,
10, 110, 106, 101, 140, 15, 38, 3, 5, 44, 7, 98, 287,
135, 150, 96, 33, 84, 125, 818, 190, 96, 520, 118,
459, 370, 653, 466, 106, 41, 107, 612, 219, 275, 30,
150, 105, 49, 53, 287, 250, 207, 134, 7, 53, 12, 47,
85, 63, 138, 110, 21, 112, 140, 495, 496, 515, 14,
73, 85, 584, 994, 150, 199, 16, 42, 5, 4, 25, 42, 8,
16, 822, 125, 159, 32, 204, 612, 818, 81, 95, 405,
41, 609, 136, 14, 20, 28, 26, 353, 302, 246, 8, 131,
159, 140, 84, 440, 42, 16, 822, 40, 67, 101, 102, 193,
138, 204, 51, 63, 240, 549, 122, 8, 10, 63, 140, 47,
48, 140, 288.

------oOo-----

No. 3.

317, 8, 92, 73, 112, 89, 67, 318, 28, 96, 107,
41, 631, 78, 146, 397, 118, 98, 114, 246, 348, 116,
74, 88, 12, 65, 32, 14, 81, 19, 76, 121, 216, 85, 33,
66, 15, '108, 68, 77, 43, 24, 122, 96, 117, 36, 211,
301, 15, 44, 11, 46, 89, 18, 136, 68, 317, 28, 90, 82,
304, 71, 43, 221, 198, 176, 310, 319, 81, 99, 264, 380,
56, 37, 319, 2, 44, 53, 28, 44, 75, 98, 102, 37, 85,
107, 117, 64, 88, 136, 48, 151, 99, 175, 89, 315, 326,
78, 96, 214, 218, 311, 43, 89, 51, 90, 75, 128, 96, 33,
28, 103, 84, 65, 26, 41, 246, 84, 270, 98, 116, 32,
59, 74, 66, 69, 240, 15, 8, 121, 20, 77, 89, 31, 11,

106, 81, 191, 224, 328, 18, 75, 52, 82, 117, 201, 39,
23, 217, 27, 21, 84, 35, 54, 109, 128, 49, 77, 88, 1,
81, 217, 64, 55, 83, 116, 251, 269, 311, 96, 54, 32,
120, 18, 132, 102, 219, 211, 84, 150, 219, 275, 312,
64, 10, 106, 87, 75, 47, 21, 29, 37, 81, 44, 18, 126,
115, 132, 160, 181, 203, 76, 81, 299, 314, 337, 351,
96, 11, 28, 97, 318, 238, 106, 24, 93, 3, 19, 17, 26,
60, 73, 88, 14, 126, 138, 234, 286, 297, 321, 365,
264, 19, 22, 84, 56, 107, 98, 123, 111, 214, 136, 7,
33, 45, 40, 13, 28, 46, 42, 107, 196, 227, 344, 198,
203, 247, 116, 19, 8, 212, 230, 31, 6, 328, 65, 48,
52, 59, 41, 122, 33, 117, 11, 18, 25, 71, 36, 45, 83,
76, 89, 92, 31, 65, 70, 83, 96, 27, 33, 44, 50, 61,
24, 112, 136, 149, 176, 180, 194, 143, 171, 205, 296,
87, 12, 44, 51, 89, 98, 34, 41, 208, 173, 66, 9, 35,
16, 95, 8, 113, 175, 90, 56, 203, 19, 177, 183, 206,
157, 200, 218, 260, 291, 305, 618, 951, 320, 18, 124,
78, 65, 19, 32, 124, 48, 53, 57, 84, 96, 207, 244, 66,
82, 119, 71, 11, 86, 77, 213, 54, 82, 316, 245, 303,
86, 97, 106, 212, 18, 37, 15, 81, 89, 16, 7, 81, 39,
96, 14, 43, 216, 118, 29, 55, 109, 136, 172, 213, 64,
8, 227, 304, 611, 221, 364, 819, 375, 128, 296, 11, 18,
53, 76, 10, 15, 23, 19, 71, 84, 120, 134, 66, 73, 89,
96, 230, 48, 77, 26, 101, 127, 936, 218, 439, 178, 171,
61, 226, 313, 215, 102, 18, 167, 262, 114, 218, 66,
59, 48, 27, 19, 13, 82, 48, 162, 119, 34, 127, 139,
34, 128, 129, 74, 63, 120, 11, 54, 61, 73, 92, 180,
66, 75, 101, 124, 265, 89, 96, 126, 274, 896, 917,
434, 461, 235, 890, 312, 413, 328, 381, 96, 105, 217,
66, 118, 22, 77, 64, 42, 12, 7, 55, 24, 83, 67, 97,
109, 121, 135, 181, 203, 219, 228, 256, 21, 34, 77,
319, 374, 382, 675, 684, 717, 864, 203, 4, 18, 92, 16,
63, 82, 22, 46, 55, 69, 74, 112, 135, 186, 175, 119,
213, 416, 312, 343, 264, 119, 186, 218, 343 , 417, 845,

*951, 124, 209, 49, 617, 856, 924, 936, 72, 19, 29,
11, 35, 42, 40, 66, 85, 94, 112, 65, 82, 115, 119,
236, 244, 186, 172, 112, 85, 6, 56, 38, 44, 85, 72,
32, 47, 73, 96, 124, 217, 314, 319, 221, 644, 817,
821, 934, 922, 416, 975, 10, 22, 18, 46, 137, 181,
101, 39, 86, 103, 116, 138, 164, 212, 218, 296, 815,
300, 412, 460, 495, 675, 820, 952.*

-----oOo----

*The papers given above were all that were contained in
the box, except two or three of an unimportant character,
and having no connection whatever with the subject in hand.
They were carefully copied, and as carefully compared with
the originals, and no error is believed to exist.*

*Complete in themselves, they are now respectfully sub-
mitted to the public with the hope that all that is dark in
them may receive light, and that the treasure, amounting, as
I figure it at this time, to more than three-quarters of a
million dollars, which has rested so long unproductive of
good, in the hands of a proper person may eventually accomplish its mission.*

*To enable my readers to understand the paper "No. 2",
the only one I was ever able to decipher. I herewith give the
Declaration of Independence, with the words numbered con-
secutively, by the assistance of which that paper's hidden
meaning was made plain:*

IN CONGRESS JULY 4, 1776.

A Declaration by the Representatives of the

UNITED STATES OF AMERICA

In General Congress Assembled.

----oOo----

1   2 3 4   5 6   7   8 9

When, in the Course of human events, it becomes

10   11 12 13   14 15   16 17   18

necessary for one people to dissolve the political bands

19 20 21   22 23 24   25 26

which have connected them with another, and to

27   28   29 30   31 32 33   34 35

assume among the Powers of the earth the separate

36 37   38   39 40   41 42   43 44   45

and equal station to which the Laws of Nature and

46 47   48 49   50   51 52   53   54 55

of Nature's God entitle them, a decent respect to the

56   57 58   59   60 61 62   63

opinions of mankind requires that they should declare

64 65   66   67   68   69 70 71

the causes which impel them to the separation.

72 73 74   75   76 77 78 79   80   81

We hold these truths to be self-evident; That all

82 83 84   85   86   87 88 89   90 91

men are created equal, that they are endowed by their

92   93 94   95   96   97 98

Creator with certain unalienable rights; that among

99   100 101 102   103 104 105   106 107

these are Life, Liberty, and the pursuit of Happiness.

108 109 110 111 112 113   114 115

That to secure these rights Governments are instituted

116   117 118   119 120 121   122 123

among Men, deriving their just powers from the

124   125 126 127   128 129   130 131   132

consent of the governed. That whenever any Form of

133   134   135   136 137 138   139

Government becomes destructive of these ends, it

140 141 142   143 144 145   146 147 148 149
is   the Right of the People to alter or to
150   151 152 153 154   155 156   157
abolish it, and to   institute new Government, laying
158 159   160 161 162   163 164   165
its foundation on such principles and organizing its
166   167 168 169   170 171 172   173 174 175
powers in such form as   to them shall seem most
176   177 178   179   180   181 182
likely to   effect their Safety and Happiness.
    183   184   185 186   187 188   189
    Prudence, indeed, will dictate that Governments long
190   191   192 193 194   195 196 197
established should not be changed for light and
198   199   200 201   202 203   204
transient causes; and, accordingly, all experience hath
205   206 207   208 209 210   211 212
shown that mankind are more disposed to suffer,
213   214 215 216   217 218 219 220   221
while evils are sufferable, than to right themselves by
222   223 224   225 226   227 228 229
abolishing the forms to which they are accustomed.
230 231   232 233 234   235 236   237 238
But, when a   long train of abuses and usurpations,
239   240   241 242 243   244   245 246
pursuing invariably the same Object, evinces a design
247 248   249 250   251   252   253 254
to reduce them under absolute Despotism, it is
255 256   257 258 259 260 261 262   263 264
their right, it is their duty to throw off such
265   266 267 268   269 270   271 272
Government, and to provide new Guards for their

273   274   275 276 277 278 279   280
future security.—Such has been the patient sufferance
281 282 283   284 285 286 287 288 289
of   these Colonies; and such is   now the necessity
290   291   292 293 294 295 296   297
which constrains them to   alter their former Systems
298 299
of   Government.
    300 301   302 303 304   305 306 307
    The history of   the present King of Great
308   309 310 311   312 313   314   315
Britain is   a   history of   repeated injuries and
316   317 318   319 320   321   322 323
usurpations, all   having in   direct object the   establish-
    324 325 326   327   328 329 330   331
ment of   an   absolute Tyranny over these States. To
332   333 334 335   336 337   338 339 340
prove this, let Facts be   submitted to   a   candid
341
world:—
    342 343 344   345 346   347 348   349 350
    He   has refused his Assent to   Laws, the most
351   352 353   354 355 356   357
wholesome and necessary for the   public good.
    358 359 360   361 362   363 364 365
    He   has forbidden his Governors to   pass Laws
366   367   368 369   370   371   372
of   immediate and pressing importance, unless sus-
    373 374 375   376 377 378   379 380
pended in   their operation till his Assent should be
381   382 383 384 385   386 387 388
obtained; and when so   suspended he   has utterly

161

389   390 391   392 393
neglected to attend to   them.

    394 395 396   397 398 399   400   401 402
    He has refused to   pass other Laws for the
403   404 405   406   407 408   409
accommodation of large districts of people, unless
410 411   412   413   414 415 416 417
those people would relinquish the right of Representa-
    418 419 420   421 422   423   424
tion in   the Legislature, a   right inestimable to
425   426 427   428 429   430
them and formidable to   Tyrants only.

    431 432 433   434   435   436   437 438
    He has called together legislative bodies at   places
439   440   441 442   443 444 445
unusual, uncomfortable, and distant from the depository
446 447 448   449   450 451 452 453   454
of   their Public Records, for the sole purpose of
455   456 457 458   459 460 461
fatiguing them into compliance with his   measures.

    462 463 464   465   466   467
    He has dissolved Representative Houses repeatedly,
468 469   470 471   472   472 474   475
for opposing with manly firmness his invasions on
476 477   478 479 480
the rights of the people.

    481 482 483   484 485 486 487   488   489
    He has refused for a   long time, after such
490   491 492   493   494 495 496   497
dissolutions to   cause others to   be   elected; whereby
498 499   500   501   502 503   504
the Legislative Powers, incapable of Annihilation, have

505   506 507 508   509 510 511 512 513
returned to the People at large for their exercise;
514 515 516   517 518 519   520   521
the State remaining, in the meantime, exposed to
522 523 524   525 526   527 528   529 530
all the dangers of invasion from without and convul-
    531
sions within.

    532 533 534   535 536   537 538   539
    He has endeavored to prevent the population of
540 541 542 543 544   545   546 547
these States; for that purpose constructing the Laws
548 549   550 551   552   553 554
for Naturalization of Foreigners; refusing to pass
555 556 557   558 559   560   561 562
others to encourage their migration hither, and raising
563 564   565 566 567   568 569
the conditions of new Appropriations of Lands.
    570 571 572   573 574   575 576
    He has obstructed the Administration of Justice,
577 578   579 580   581 582 583 584
by refusing his Assent to Laws for establishing
585   586
Judiciary Powers.
    587 588 589 590   591   592 593 594
    He has made Judges dependent on his Will
595 596 597 598 599 600 601   602 603
alone, for the tenure of their offices, and the
604 605 606   607 608 609
amount and payment of their salaries.
    610 611 612 613 614   615 616 617
    He has erected a multitude of New Offices,

618 619 620   621   622 623   624 625   626
and sent hither swarms of   Officers to   harass our
627   628 629 630 631   632
People, and eat out their substance.

633 634 635   636   637 638 639   640 641
He has kept among us, in times of   peace,
642   643   644   645 646   647 648 649
Standing Armies, without the consent of   our legislature.

650   651   652   653   654   655
He   has   affected   to   render   the
656   657   658 659 660   661 662 663
Military independent of   and superior to   the Civil
664
Power.

665 666 667   668   669   670 671   672 673
He has combined with others to   subject us   to
674 675   676   677 678 679   680 681
a   jurisdiction foreign to   our constitution and unack-
682 683 684   685   686 687   688 689
nowledged by our laws; giving his   assent to   their
690 691 692   693
acts of   pretended legislation.

694 695   696   697   698 699   700
For quartering large bodies of   armed troops
701   702
among us.

703 704   705   706 707 708   709   710
For protecting them, by   a   mock Trial, from
711   712 713 714   715   716 717   718
Punishment for any Murders which they should commit

164

719 720 721   722 723 724
on   the Inhabitants of   these States.

    725 726   727 728 729   730 731 732   733 734
    For cutting off our Trade with all   parts of   the
735
world.

    736 737   738   739 740 741   742 743
    For imposing taxes on   us   without our Consent.
    744 745   746 747 748   749   750 751 752
    For depriving us, in   many cases, of   the benefits
753 754   755 756
of Trial by Jury.

    757 758   759 760   761   762 763 764
    For transporting us beyond Seas to be   tried
765 766   767
for pretended offences.

    768 769   770 771 772   773 774   775
    For abolishing the free System of   English Laws
776 777 778   779   780   781   782
in a   neighboring Province, establishing therein an
783   784   785 786   787 788   789
Arbitrary government, and enlarging its Boundaries so
790 791 792   793 794 795 796 797   798 799
as to render it at   once an example and fit
800   801 802   803 804   805   806 807
instrument for introducing the same absolute rule in
808   809
these Colonies.

    810 811   812 813 814   815   816 817
    For taking away our Charters, abolishing our most
818   819 820 821   822   823 824
valuable Laws, and altering fundamentally the Forms

825 826 827
of   our Governments.

828 829   830 831 832   833 834
For suspending our own Legislature, and declaring

835   836   837 838   839 840   841 842
themselves invested with Power to   legislate for us

843 844 845 846
in   all   case whatsoever.

847 848 849   850   851   852 853
He has abdicated Government here, by declaring

854 855 856 857 858   859 860   861 862
us   out of his protection, and waging War against

863
us.

864 865 866   867 868   869   870 871
He has plundered our seas, ravaged our Coasts,

872   873 874   875 876   877 878 879 880
burnt our towns, and destroyed the lives of   our

881
people.

882 883 884 885 886 887   888   889
He is   at   this time transporting large armies

890 891   892   893 894   895 896   897
of foreign mercenaries to   compleat the works of

898   899   900 901   902   903   904 905
death, desolation and tyranny, already begun with cir-

        906 907   908 909   910   911
cumstances of cruelty &   perfidy scarcely paralleled

912 913 914 915   916 917 918   919   920
in   the most barbarous ages, and totally unworthy the

921 922 923 924   925
head of a   civilized nation.

926 927 928   929 930   931   932   933
He has constrained our fellow citizens taken Cap-
934 935 936 937   938 939 940   941   942
tive on the high Seas to   bear Arms against their
943   944 945   946 947   948 949 950
Country, to   become the executioners of   their friends
951 952   953 954 955 956   957 958   959
and Brethren, or   to fall themselves by   their Hands.
960 961 962   963   964   965   966
He has excited domestic insurrections amongst us,
967 968 969   970 971   972 973 974   975
and has endeavored to   bring on   the inhabitants of
976 977   978 979   980   981   982
our frontiers, the merciless Indian Savages, whose
983   984 985 986   987 988 989
known rule of   warfare is   an   undistinguished
990   991 992 993   994   995 996
destruction of all   ages, sexes, and conditions.
997 998   999   1000 1001 1002   1003 1004
In   every stage of   these Oppressions We   have
1005   1006 1007   1008 1009 1010 1011   1012
Petitioned for   Redress in   the   most humble terms.
1013 1014   1015   1016 1017 1018   1019 1020
Our repeated Petitions have been answered only by
1021   1022
repeated injury.
1023 1024   1025 1026   1027 1028 1029
A   Prince whose character is   thus marked
1030 1031 1032 1033   1034 1035 1036 1037   1038
by   every act   which may define a   Tyrant is
1039 1040 1041 1042 1043 1044 1045 1046 1047
unfit to   be   the   ruler of   a   free people.

1048 1049 1050 1051 1052   1053 1054   1055
Nor   have we   been wanting in   attentions to
1056 1057   1058   1059 1060 1061   1062 1063
our British brethren. We   have warned them from
1064 1065 1066 1067 1068   1069 1070 1071
time to   time of   attempts by   their legislature
1072 1073   1074 1075   1076   1077 1078
to   extend an   unwarrantable jurisdiction over us.
1079 1080 1081   1082 1083 1084 1085
We   have reminded them of   the   circumstances
1086 1087 1088   1089 1090   1091 1092 1093
of   our   emigration and settlement here. We have
1094   1095 1096 1097   1098   1099 1100
appealed to   their native justice and magnanimity,
1101 1102 1103 1104   1105 1106 1107 1108 1109
and we   have conjured them by   the   ties   of
1110 1111   1112   1113 1114   1115 1116
our   common kindred to   disavow these usurpations,
1117 1118 1119   1120   1121 1122   1123
which would inevitably interrupt our connections and
1124   1125 1126 1127 1128 1129 1130 1131
correspondence. They, too, have been deaf to   the
1132 1133 1134   1135 1136 1137
voice of   justice and of   consanguinity.
      1138 1139 1140   1141   1142 1143 1144
We   must, therefore, acquiesce in   the   necessity
1145 1146   1147 1148   1149 1150 1151
which denounces our Separation, and   hold them,
1152 1153 1154 1155 1156 1157 1158   1159
as   we   hold the   rest of   mankind; Enemies
1160 1161 1162 1163   1164
in   War; in   Peace, Friends.

168

1165 1166   1167 1168   1169 1170
We, therefore, the Representatives of the
1171 1172 1173 1174   1175 1176   1177
United States of America, in General Congress
1178   1179   1180 1181 1182   1183 1184
Assembled, appealing to the Supreme Judge of
1185 1186 1187 1188 1189   1190 1191 1192
the world for the rectitude of our intentions,
1193 1194 1195 1196 1197 1198 1199   1200 1201
do, in the Name and by Authority of the
1202 1203 1204 1205 1206   1207   1208   1209
good People of these Colonies, solemnly publish and
1210 1211 1212 1213   1214   1215 1216 1217
declare that these United Colonies are, and of
1218 1219 1220 1221 1222 1223 1224   1225
Right ought to be, Free and Independent States;
1226 1227 1228 1229   1230 1231 1232   1233
that they are Absolved from all Allegiance to
1234 1235 1236   1237 1238 1239 1240   1241
the British Crown, and that all political connection
1242   1243 1244 1245 1246 1247 1248 1249   1250
between them and the State of Great Britain is,
1251 1252 1253 1254 1255 1256   1257 1258 1259
and ought to be, totally dissolved; and that, as
1260 1261 1262   1263   1264 1265 1266 1267
Free and Independent States, they have full Power
1268 1269 1270 1271   1272   1273   1274
to levy war, conclude Peace, contract Alliances,
1275   1276   1277 1278 1279 1280 1281 1282
establish Commerce, and to do all other Acts
1283 1284 1285 1286   1287 1288 1289 1290
and Things which Independent States may of right

169

1291
do.

    1292 1293 1294 1295   1296 1297 1298
    And for the support of   this Declaration,
1299 1300 1301 1302   1303 1304 1305   1306
with a   firm reliance on   the Protection of
1307   1308   1309 1310   1311   1312 1313
Divine Providence we   mutually pledge to   each
1314 1315 1316   1317 1318   1319 1320 1321
other our   Lives, our   Fortunes, and our   sacred
1322
Honor.

---oOo---

    'I furnish herewith a translation of Paper No. 2, indicating of what the treasure consists, based upon the use of the Declaration of Independence as the key:

I	*h*	*a*	*v*	*e*	*D*	*e*	*p*	*o*	*s*
115	73	24	818	37	52	49	17	31	62

i	*t*	*e*	*d*	*i*	*n*	*t*	*h*	*e*	*C*	*o*
657	22	7	15	140	47	29	107	79	84	56

u	*n*	*t*	*y*	*o*	*f*	*B*	*e*	*d*	*f*	*o*
238	10	26	822	5	195	308	85	52	159	136

r	*d*	*a*	*b*	*o*	*u*	*t*	*f*	*o*	*u*	*r*
49	210	36	0	46	316	543	122	106	95	53

m	*i*	*l*	*e*	*s*	*f*	*r*	*o*	*m*	*B*	*u*	*f*
58	2	42	7	35	122	53	31	82	77	250	195

o	*r*	*d*	*s*	*i*	*n*	*a*	*n*	*e*	*x*
56	96	118	71	140	287	28	353	37	994

c	*a*	*v*	*a*	*t*	*i*	*o*	*n*	*o*	*r*	*v*	*a*
65	147	818	24	3	8	12	47	43	59	818	45

u l t s i x f e e t
316 101 41 78 154 994 122 138 190 16

b e l o w t h e s u r
77 49 102 57 72 34 73 85 35 371 59

f a c e o f t h e g
195 81 92 190 106 273 60 394 629 270

r o u n d t h e f o l
219 106 388 287 63 3 6 190 122 43 233

l o w i n g a r t i c
400 106 290 314 47 48 81 96 26 115 92

l e s b e l o n g i n
157 190 110 77 85 196 46 10 113 140 353

g j o i n t l y t o
48 120 106 2 616 61 420 822 29 125

t h e p a r t i e s w
14 26 37 105 28 248 16 158 7 35 19

h o s e n a m e s a
301 125 110 496 287 98 117 520 62 51

r e g i v e n i n n
219 37 113 140 818 138 549 8 44 287

u m b e r t h r e e h
388 117 18 79 344 34 20 59 520 557 107

e r e w i t h.
612 219 37 66 154 41 20

T h e f i r s t d e
50 6 584 122 154 248 110 61 52 33

p o s i t c o n s i s t
30 5 38 8 14 84 57 549 216 115 71 29

e d o f t e n h u n d
85 63 43 131 29 138 47 73 238 549 52

r e d a n d f o u r t
53 79 118 51 44 63 195 12 238 112 3

171

e   e   n   p   o   u   n   d   s   o
49 79 353   105 56 371 566 210 515   125

f g o l d a n d t h
360 133 143 101 15   284 549 252   14 204

i r t y e i g h t h
140 344 26 822   138 115 48 73 34   204

u n d r e d a n d t w
316 616 63 219 7 52   150 44 52   16 40

e l v e p o u n d s o
37 157 818 37   121 12 95 10 15 35   12

f s i l v e r d e p
131   62 115 102 818 49 53   135 138 30

o s i t e d N o v e i
31 62 67 41 85 63   10 106 818   138 8

g h t e e n n i n e t
113 20 32 33 37 353   287 140 47 85 50

e e n.
37 49 47

T h e s e c o n d w a s
64 6 7   71 33 4 43 47 63   1 27 609

m a d e D e c e i g h
207 229 15 190   246 85 94   520 2 270 20

t e e n t w e n t y o n
39 7 33 44   22 40 7 10 3 822   106 44

e a n d c o n s i s
496   229 353 210   199 31 10 38 140 297

t e d o f n i n e t e
61 612 329   302 676   287 2 44 33 32 520

e n h u n d r e d a n
557 10   6 250 566 246 53 37 52   83 47

172

d	s	e	v	e	n	p	o	u	n	d	s
320	38	33	818	7	44	30	31	250	10	15	35

o	f	g	o	l	d	a	n	d	t
106	159	113	31	102	406	229	549	320	29

w	e	l	v	e	h	u	n	d	r	e
66	33	101	818	138	301	316	353	320	219	37

d	a	n	d	e	i	g	h	t	y	e
52	28	549	320	33	8	49	107	50	822	7

i	g	h	t	o	f	s	i	l	v	e
2	113	73	16	125	11	110	67	102	818	33

r;	a	l	s	o	j	e	w	e	l	s
59	81	157	38	43	590	138	19	85	400	38

o	b	t	a	i	n	e	d	i	n	S	t.
43	77	14	27	8	47	138	63	140	44	33	22

L	o	u	i	s	i	n	e	x	c	h
176	106	250	314	216	2	10	7	994	4	20

a	n	g	e	t	o	s	a	v	e	t
25	44	48	7	26	46	110	229	818	190	34

r	a	n	s	p	o	r	t	a	t	i	o
112	147	44	110	121	125	96	41	51	50	140	56

n	a	n	d	v	a	l	u	e	d
47	152	549	63	818	28	42	250	138	591

a	t	t	h	i	r	t	e	e	n	t
98	653	32	107	140	112	26	85	138	549	50

h	o	u	s	a	n	d	d	o	l	l
20	125	371	38	36	10	52	118	136	102	420

a	r	s.
150	112	71

T	h	e	a	b	o	v	e	i	s
14	20	7	24	18	13	818	37	67	110

s	e	c	u	r	e	l	y	p	a	c
62	33	21	95	219	520	102	822	30	83	84

k	e	d	i	n	i	r	o	n	p
305	620	15	2	10	8	219	106	353	105

o	t	s	w	i	t	h	i	r	o	n
106	60	242	72	8	50	204	184	112	125	549

c	o	v	e	r	s.	T	h	e	v	a
65	106	818	190	96	110	16	73	53	818	150

u	l	t	i	s	r	o	u	g	h
409	400	50	154	285	96	106	316	270	204

l	y	l	i	n	e	d	w	i	t	h
101	822	400	8	44	37	52	40	240	34	204

s	t	o	n	e	a	n	d	t	h	e	v
38	16	46	47	85	24	44	15	64	73	138	818

e	s	s	e	l	s	r	e	s	t	o
85	78	110	33	420	515	55	37	38	22	31

n	s	o	l	i	d	s	t	o	n	e
10	110	106	101	140	15	38	3	5	44	7

a	n	d	a	r	e	c	o	v	e
98	287	135	150	96	33	84	125	818	190

r	e	d	w	i	t	h	o	t	h
96	520	118	459	370	653	466	106	41	107

e	r	s.
612	219	275

P	a	p	e	r	n	u	m	b	e
30	150	105	49	53	287	250	207	134	7

r	o	n	e	d	e	s	c	r	i	b
53	12	47	85	63	138	110	21	112	140	495

e	s	t	h	e	e	x	a	c	t
496	515	14	73	85	584	994	150	199	16

l	o	c	a	l	i	t	y	o	f	t	h
42	5	4	25	42	8	16	822	125	159	32	204

e	v	a	u	l	t	s	o	t	h
612	818	81	95	405	41	609	136	14	20

```
a    t    n    o     d    i   f    f    i    c    u
28   26   353  302   246  8   131  159  140  84   440
l    t    y    w    i    l    l     b    e    h
42   16   822  40   67   101  102   193  138  204
a    d    i    n     f    i   n    d    i    n    g
51   63   240  549   122  8   10   63   140  47   48
i    t.
140  288
```

In preparing his cipher No. 2 Beale used the initial letter of each numbered word referred to, except—

> *Word 822, fundamentally, he used the final letter, y.*
> *Word 994, sexes, he used the medial letter, x.*
> *Word 95, inalienable is spelled by Thomas Jefferson with a "u," so that Beale properly found a word in the Declaration of Independence beginning with "u."*

In conclusion, it may not be inappropriate to say a few words regarding myself: In consequence of the time lost in the above investigation I have been reduced from comparative affluence to absolute penury, entailing suffering upon those it was my duty to protect; and this, too, in spite of their remonstrances. My eyes were at last opened to their condition, and I resolved to sever at once, and forever, all connection with the affair, and retrieve, if possible, my errors. To do this, and as the best means of placing temptation beyond my reach, I determined to make public the whole matter, and shift from my shoulders my responsibility to Mr. Morriss.

I anticipate for these papers a large circulation, and, to avoid the multitude of letters with which I should be assailed, from all sections of the Union, propounding all sorts of questions and requiring answers which, if attended to, would absorb my entire time, and only change the character of my work, I have decided upon withdrawing my name from the publication, after assuring all interested that I have given all that I know of the matter, and that I cannot add one word to the statements herein contained.

The gentleman whom I have selected as my agent to publish and circulate these papers, was well known to Mr. Morriss; it was at his house that Mrs. Morriss died, and he would have been one of the beneficiaries in the event of my success. Like every one else, he was ignorant of this episode in Mr. Morriss' career until the manuscript was placed in his hands.

Trusting that he will be benefitted by the arrangement, which I know would have met the approval of Mr. Morriss, I have left the whole subject to his sole management and charge. All business communications should be addressed to him. It is needless to say that I shall await with much anxiety the development of the mystery.

The chimney — all that remains of Buford's Tavern

George L. Hart, Sr.

The Hart Papers

(Presenting details of an alleged
burial of gold, silver and jewels near
Goose Creek, Bedford County, Virginia,
by Thomas Jefferson Beale and associates
in November 1819 and December 1821.)
by

George L. Hart, Sr.,

in an attempt to bring up-to-date
all that is known and surmised
about the subject.

As of the present date, January 1, 1952, the writer will make an effort to put in writing all that he knows or surmises about the above subject, study and work upon which he spent many hours, yes, a total of many months, extending over a period from 1898 to 1912, more or less in collaboration with his brother, the late Clayton I. Hart, of Roanoke, Virginia.

Along in the summer of 1897 my brother, then a stenographer in the office of the Auditor of the Norfolk & Western Railroad, Roanoke, Va., was requested by the chief clerk to the Auditor, N. H. Hazlewood, then residing at Montvale, (formerly Buford) Bedford County, Virginia, to make several copies of eight sheets of notepaper, two sheets headed simply "No. 1", three sheets headed "No. 2", and three sheets headed "No. 3".

Curiosity impelled Clayton to ask Mr. Hazlewood what such figures, most unusual in his experience in the office, could possibly mean. In the beginning of their conversation Mr. Hazlewood stated that they were connected with a treasure, said to have been buried some four score years before near the foot of the Peaks of Otter, which stood in all their majesty overlooking his residence; and that, so far as he knew, said treasure had never been located. Clayton obtained permission to retain a copy of the three ciphers or criptograms.

Clayton immediately began studying the meaningless figures, discussing with Mr. Hazlewood from time to time this or that possibility; however, neither getting anywhere near the beginning of a solution. In a few months Mr. Hazlewood's health began to fail, whereupon he expressed an intention to give no further attention to the mystery, passing it on to Clayton with the admonition: "Go ahead on your own. I wish you success. Even though I have never made any headway in the matter of deciphering the figures, I remain reasonably confident the treasure lies buried where originally placed.

About that time Clayton learned that a man by the name of Ward had spent many years trying to find a key, or keys, to the ciphers; that he had found a key to one cipher, but had finally abandoned his efforts and published in pamphlet form all that he knew about the treasure.

Thereupon, Clayton journeyed to Lynchburg, Va., 50 miles east of Roanoke, secured a copy of the printed pamphlet, and redoubled his efforts to find a solution.

The preceding manuscript was prepared by James B. Ward, of Campbell County, Virginia, contiguous to Lynchburg, in the year 1884. It was printed in pamphlet form by the Virginian Job Print, Lynchburg, Va. However, Clayton was informed by Ward that all but a few copies had been destroyed by fire, which broke out in the printing plant before a plan of distribution and sale at 50 cents a copy had been made and carried out.

About the year 1903 Clayton visited Mr. Ward, who then was at an advanced age. He confirmed all that is contained in the pamphlet; and his son, then U.S. Mail transfer clerk at the union station, Lynchburg, added his own confirmation, but in somewhat sad and solemn tones. Both are long since deceased.

The writer, and his brother Clayton, from 1897 until 1907, put in practically every moment of their spare time in an effort to find a key, or keys, for the two ciphers which are as yet meaningless. Residing then at Roanoke, Va., fourteen miles west of Montvale, (formerly Buford) Bedford County, Virginia, frequent trips were made by one or other of us, both of us together sometimes, to the supposed general location of the alleged buried treasure. And, on visits to Lynchburg, whence we journeyed occasionally on professional work, we secured confirmation as to the Washington Hotel, and its proprietor, Mr. Morriss, during the period 1819 to 1862.

My brother Clayton and I, separately and jointly, turned to the Constitution, Shakespeare, the Declaration of Independence, and numerous other books and documents that we thought might have been in the library of the Washington Hotel, at Lynchburg, during Beale's sojourn there. We numbered the words forward and backward, finally skipping the first word and beginning with the second, then starting with the third word, fourth and fifth words, then taking every fifth word, tenth word, etc. However, we found no solution.

In 1898 my brother Clayton became interested in mesmerism and hypnotism. He wondered if this might be the means of securing a lead. Finding an excellent subject, who gradually drifted into crystal reading, Clayton began questioning him about the alleged treasure. Thinking he was, by this means, securing a worthwhile lead, Clayton asked the writer to sit in on a seance. The result of sitting will be given in detail near the end of this story. Of course, the writer, then as now, placed no faith in what came forth so glibly from the mouth of the crystal reader. But, like a drowning man, we were catching at any straws that might float about.

So, when the subject, during his trance, claimed he could see not only the alleged buried treasure, but would be able to lead us to it, we determined to test him out.

One nice Spring evening in 1899, the writer and his brother departed from Roanoke about five o'clock p.m. in the family buggy, drawn by the faithful family horse, Old Nell. We carried what we believed to be the necessary equipment, (other than dynamite, with which I would have no part), that equipment including picks, shovels, lanterns, rope, an axe, etc. And with us, of course, was our confident crystal reader—that is, confident to the Nth degree when he was gazing into the crystal ball.

We drove by "The Great Lick", a mile to the east of our old homestead, which, it was claimed, in the colonial days attracted wild animals desiring salt; on east through the gap of the Blue Ridge Mountains, to the tavern location in the village known in 1819-22 as Buford, (now Montvale) said tavern supposed to have been visited by Beale and his associates while seeking a place to bury the alleged treasure, and the subsequent trip.

Darkness had settled over the land, as we had expected,

182

and which the better suited our purpose. Few people were moving about, and the faint light of a receding moon afforded opportunity to see objects of any size, which was just what we wanted.

Driving across the railroad track, in the direction of the Peaks of Otter, we stopped on reaching a clump of bushes and many trees, about a mile up Goose Creek. My brother and the subject alighted, the subject was hypnotized, and they started off along Goose Creek, I following in the buggy. The trail led toward a gap in the mountain that would, if followed, take one over into Botetourt County.

And, it might not be amiss to pause here and explain, that in the town of Buchanan, just over the mountain, there lived a quite prominent family of the name of Beale, who owned a plantation bordering on the James River.

But, to resume our narrative: About four miles up Goose Creek the subject stopped, seemed to be taking his bearings, then climbed a rail fence, jumped across a spring branch, ascended a hill, walked over the top and down into a crater-like place, covered with old oak trees and many leaves. Halting by the side of a large oak the subject pointed to the ground at its base and exclaimed: "There's the treasure! Can't you see it?"

Well, had we finally reached the promised land? We did not believe it possible, and yet there was a certain plausibility about the confidence of the subject, so we took stock of our situation and planned our work. Lighting another lantern, we placed one on each side of the spot pointed out to us, and while one brother assembled the tools, the other walked up to the top of the crater-like place, and then down around the spot, to judge how much of the light from our lanterns might be seen in the neighborhood.

Satisfied of our safety from intrusion, we agreed that each brother would dig, or shovel, for 10 minutes, then to be

183

relieved by the other brother. This was to be continued until we located the treasure, or were satisfied that it did not rest there. In the meantime the subject was relieved of his trance, and he lay down in the leaves, apparently wondering what we were about, but otherwise showing no interest.

We diligently set to work digging. After some six hours or more, in the wee small hours of the following morning, we had succeeded in digging a hole approximately six feet in depth, and slightly larger than a grave. Our strength was about gone, we were filled with misgivings, and, then, when about 8 of the 10 minutes of my brother's turn had been used, his pick struck a rock that produced a hollow sound. He looked up at me, his eyes flashing the fire of hope, and I, in my own enthusiasm, said: "You're played out! Permit me to relieve you now!" But, no, he replied: "Let me finish my allotted time".

After awhile we succeeded in removing the rock, but the hoped-for pots of gold and silver were not underneath it. Now, were we let down? To relieve our chagrin the subject was again hypnotized and asked to reveal the whereabouts of the treasure. Rising on the balls of his feet, as if in disgust, he pointed to the left about two feet, directly underneath the great oak tree, and exclaimed: "There it is! You got over too far! Can't you see it?"

Thereupon I was completely let-down, and unwilling to make any further attempt, certainly so far as that trip was concerned. Crestfallen, we wended our way back home. A week or two later my brother returned to the spot alone, I refusing to accompany him. He provided himself with dynamite, and upon his return home he informed me that he blasted out the old tree, and about everything near it—but, still no pots of gold, silver and jewels.

Was there anything more that we should and could do? After a short lapse of time my brother and I held a conference. We reviewed all that we had done, or attempted to do, and tried to map out a plan of future action, if any, we should take. We agreed that we had never heard that a person could transfer to the mind of a hypnotized subject, his own beliefs or knowledge, and get the subject to repeat them; yet we wondered if, after all, that was, in part at least, what had occurred. Certainly Clayton had never been anywhere near the spot to which the subject led us; nor had he any thought that Beale and his party had gone there while seeking a place to hide their treasure. So, why did the subject lead us to that spot? We could not then, nor do we now, find any satisfactory answer. Like many other questions that flash through one's mind, there seems no way to turn in the hope of getting the mystery cleared up.

Subsequent to my visit to the spot pointed out by the subject, I gave less and less time to a study of the ciphers; and, about 1912, I ceased altogether. Clayton, on the other hand, made many visits to the spot, and continued his interest in the ciphers until his death September 6, 1949.

In 1919 I moved to Washington, D.C., and began the practice of my profession in that city, where, until 1946, I was extremely busy, night and day. So, after 1919, I only gave casual thought to the subject; now and then going back and reading over my old papers, and writing to some one, or talking with some one about it.

In the December, 1924, number of THE AMERICAN I read an article about Colonel George Fabyan, of Riverbank Laboratories, Geneva, Ill., and his success during World War I, and since, in reading code messages. I wrote to him, sending a copy of the three ciphers; and, after some correspondence back and forth, I forwarded to him a copy of such data as I had, but with special request that he not make any use of the manuscript, or ciphers, other than an attempt to decipher the ciphers. I made this request because my brother

185

Clayton, then living, was trying to prepare something for publication, which he never did.

Under date of February 3, 1925, Colonel Fabyan replied, and, among other things of no special interest to me, said:

"Now, in reference to the three ciphers: It seems improbable to us that a cipher of this character could be deciphered by a novice without the key, regardless of whether he put 20 years or 40 years on it. The cipher would be classified as a complex substitution cipher—variable-key system, or pseudo code; and even though one were told that the Declaration of Independence was the key, unless it was intimated as to how it was used as a key, we think that the novice would have been utterly baffled as to how to use it. The stumbling of a novice upon a method of this character lies rather beyond the range of possibility, and the conviction follows that they were in possession of the key of not only No. 2, but also of No. 1 and No. 3, with the result that the treasure referred to has long since been removed and converted.

"I repeat, that the problem has my interest, and I am writing in the vain hope that either you or Clayton I. Hart can give us further information, because the psychology of it is about all we have to go on in picking out our point of attack. In the meantime we will retain the pamphlet, and work on it as we can find time to do so."

But I never heard further from Colonel Fabyan, and assume that he was unable to do anything toward clearing up the mystery.

As I often said to my brother, and wrote to Colonel Fabyan, it is possible that the whole thing is without basis. I have wondered if Ward might have written his manuscript based upon some figures he found, or made up; and yet, we have the word of Ward, his son, and friends to the contrary.

Inquiry among some aged neighbors of Ward showed the high respect they had for him, and brought forth the statement that Ward would never practice deception.

Just as a little sidelight on the ramifications of this work, I will add the following: In 1917 my wife asked me to drive her down for a visit to her first cousin, Mr. Otey, near Montvale, formerly Buford. On arrival at Montvale we were directed to drive along Goose Creek, cross that stream at the first crossing, and drive up the other side, when we would reach Mr. Otey's place. All of which we did. While sitting out on the porch enjoying a glass of lemonade, I remarked that some years before I had had occasion to drive up the old road, on the other side of the creek, in a buggy. Being asked the occasion for such a visit, I told him the story of our digging. He laughed, loud and long, telling me it cleared up a mystery that had worried the people along the creek for upwards of 20 years. He stated that after the first hole we dug was discovered, some of his neighbors watched all night for a few days, armed with shotguns; and that after what was described as "the great explosion", a watch was again set for a week or 10 days, without result.

I have often wondered what became of the key, or keys, to the ciphers, left by Beale with some friend in St. Louis, when he was there in 1822, and visited the Planters Hotel.

When my brother Clayton secured a copy of the printed pamphlet containing Ward's story about the Beale papers, I think in the summer of 1898, he asked me to read same two or three times and then sit down and discuss the subject with him. This I did. We were at a loss to know how to begin any new or untried effort to unravel the mystery.

That Ward, by accident as he suggests, succeeded in finding a key to cipher No. 2, outlining the number of pounds of gold and silver, along with jewels of a value of $13,000, claimed to have been buried, created a suspicion that the story might have been made up instead of founded on fact, with the idea of finding a more ready sale of the pamphlet. Beale's letter to Mr. Morriss, accompanying the ciphers, did not state which of the three ciphers described the place of concealment, but one would think that cipher No. 1 would be the starting point and have the most attention.

And why would Beale go to the trouble to prepare three ciphers, each based upon a different document?

If the story was not based upon fact but something prepared with the idea of making money from the sale of it, why was it allowed to remain in the printing plant until an accidental fire consumed practically all copies of it?

I suggested that my brother Clayton make a trip to Lynchburg and secure any information within reach, visiting Ward if he could locate him. He made several trips, and inquired all round the town, becoming cconvinced that it was more than probable the story was founded upon fact.

Thereupon Clayton redoubled his efforts to find a key, or keys, to Ciphers No. 1 and No. 3. He worked every night for upwards of two years without making any headway, but, like Ward, was unwilling to lay the subject aside.

Having studied hypnotism and mesmerism, which had become somewhat of a fad in Roanoke about that time, as a result of several demonstrations on the stage of the Academy of Music, Clayton began to try out his powers on numerous promising subjects. Finding one exceptionally good subject, in the person of an eighteen-year-old lad in the neighborhood of our old home, Magnolia, on the extreme northern line of the City of Roanoke, Va., he, after a time, tried him out as a crystal reader or clairvoyant.

To Clayton's astonishment the boy, while in a state of trance, related a wonderful story, one which fitted in so well with what he had learned about the treasure that he determined to unravel the mystery, if possible, through that means. So he invited me to witness a seance and tell him what I thought of what I would see and hear.

The subject was a quiet, unassuming, diffident boy. In his normal state he seemed quite effeminate, and never indulged in the use of profane language. Under the spell, however, he seemed transformed into a vigorous, determined man of the world, confident of himself, swearing blandly, and ready to meet all comers. The following is an account of that incident, written by me some ten years thereafter at the request of my brother, Clayton. I had no notes made at the time, so this account came purely from memory—and may be more or less inaccurate. However, the following depicts the occurrence as I remembered it, with Clayton acting as interrogator, I being merely a quiet listener and observer.

A Crystal Reading.

"Jewels, By Gosh! Diamonds! Rubies! Pearls! Emeralds! Whew! Ain't the old man rich?"

These and other similar exclamations came from the lips of medium as he gazed into the crystal ball. Oblivious of his surroundings, apparently in a trance, eyes bulging, features tense, a death-like grip on what was opaque to the bystander, but which, when revolved in the hands of the medium, like the earth on its axis, seemed an inspiration, the clairvoyant quickly turned back the pages of time to a century before, and claimed to read events then taking place. I stepped into the dimly lighted room, on the second floor of our old home, Magnolia, just after the medium had entered the state of trance, and while my brother, Clayton, was commanding:

"Time is moving backward quite fast, and will continue so moving until you reach November 1819. Go to Buford's Tavern, in a village of that name just to the east of the Blue

Ridge Mountains, and watch for the coming of several prairie schooners. Tell me as soon as they come in sight, and relate everything that those in charge do. Now, tell me everything they have with them, and everything they do. Keep close watch on them, and don't let them get out of your sight!''

Within about thirty seconds the medium straightened up, and, trembling as if from excitement, began to talk:

"Here they come! They're just passing through the gap in the mountain.

"Watch them carefully! Don't let them get out of your sight! How many wagons or prairie schooners do you see?

"I see five covered wagons.

"Are there any men riding horses, or mules, accompanying the wagons?

"Yes; five men on horses.

"How many men are there altogether?

"Let me see? (As if counting on his fingers) There's ten; five men driving the wagons and five men on horseback.

"Where are they riding in reference to the wagons? I mean, are they in front of the wagons, by the side of the wagons, or in the rear of the wagons?

"A big, fine looking fellow is riding alone in front, two men are riding abreast just in his rear, followed by the five men driving the wagons, and two men are riding abreast at the rear of the wagons.

"Have the men any guns or pistols?

"Sure! Each man riding horseback has a rifle slung across the front of his saddle, with two pistols in leather containers slung from his belt, one to his right hand, the other to his left hand.

"How about the men driving the wagons?

"Each driver has a rifle and a couple of pistols on the seat beside him. Oh! They're fixed for game, and, I reckon, for Indians, too!

190

"Watch them carefully and tell me if they stop anywhere?

There was silence for a minute or two, when Clayton stepped up the time with a command.

"They've done stopped.

"Where?

"At a place that has a board up over the door and on it marked 'Tavern'. And, on a little building right by the side of it, I see another board which says 'Buford Post Office'. And I see a few other houses scattered about.

"Watch them carefully and tell me everything they do.

"The big fellow, the one who was riding in front, and I guess he is the boss of the outfit, has done got off his horse, handed the reins to another fellow, and gone into the tavern.

"Watch them closely and tell me all that is done.

"The boss is talking to some man inside the tavern. I guess he's asking can he take care of his men and horses. Anyhow the tavern-keeper smiles and bows his head, pushing forward a much-worn book. The boss man is writing in it.

"What are they doing now?

"They are driving around to the stable. The boss man has taken his saddlebags off his horse, turned the bridle reins over to an old gray-haired Negro, and has done gone into the tavern.

"Don't let him get out of your sight! Watch him closely, and tell me all that he does!

"The boss man's done gone upstairs. It's nearly dark. A Negro slave is showing him to a room. But the big fellow wouldn't let the Negro carry his saddlebags. The Negro is looking at him as if he thinks it's mighty unusual doings for a gentleman. I guess in those days Negro slaves were expected to do everything for a guest except spit.

"Well, never mind about your wise cracks. Keep a close watch on the big fellow! Don't let him get out of your sight! What is he doing?

191

"He's done raised the window and is motioning to one of his pals, who is out in the yard, to come up to his room. That fellow is not going up the steps, and is entering the room. The boss man is talking, motioning to his saddle bags, and is now going back down the steps, while the other man stays in the room. He's done gone in and sat down at the supper table.

"Time is passing a little faster now. Tell me what the boss man, as you term him, is doing.

"He's done gone back upstairs to his room. He's motioning the other fellow to go out of the room; I guess he's telling him to go downstairs and get his grub.

"Watch the boss man carefully, now, and tell me everything he does. Time is passing more slowly, remember!

The boss man is pulling down the shades. My! Those shades are on strings; they don't roll down like shades do nowadays, on springs. He's locking the door; and, by gosh! don't you know, he's stuffing some paper into the keyhole. No wonder, for the keyhole is almost as big as three fingers of a man's hand. The key must be mighty big. Yes, it is, for I see it there on the table.

"Well, go along and tell me what that man is doing.

"Now he's putting his old big pistol on the table, right by the side of the candle. He's laying his saddlebags across the bed, and is unstrapping both sides. I wonder if he is hunting for a bottle of rum?

"Never mind about any bottle. Watch that man closely, and tell me everything he does?

"My God! The old man is opening up a regular diamond mine! They glitter so they hurt my eyes. I didn't know there was so many fine jewels in all the world. It beats any jeweler's show case I ever saw.

"Tell me about what he has. What do you see?

"Jewels, By Gosh! Diamonds! Rubies! Pearls!

Emeralds! Whew! Ain't that big fellow some pumpkins?

And the subject shaded his eyes with his hands, as though the brilliance of the precious stones was dazzling him; and, all the while he was turning his head to right and to left, as if either to see more or to shake away the sight he was beholding.

"Keep close watch on the big fellow and tell me everything he does", Clayton admonished.

"Now, he's wrapping up the jewels in something that looks like fine skins, and putting them back into his saddlebags. He's putting the saddlebags under the pillow, between featherbed and pillows, and has thrown the bolster off onto a chair. He's undressing, but he ain't taking off all of his clothes. Now he's reading the Bible, which was lying on the table.

"Time is passing more quickly now. Tell me what the boss man, as you call him, does before he snuffs the candle?

"He's done replaced the Bible on the table. He's snuffing out the candle. The room is now dark.

"Go out to the stable and tell me what is being done by his companions out there?" Clayton suggested.

"The horses are in stalls, munching hay. The five prairie schooners are parked in a row, between the horse stable and the cow stable. There's a man sitting in each wagon, the men being, in each case, in the front of one wagon and in the rear of the adjoining wagon. Each man has two pistols in his belt, with a rifle at his side. Now, that's damn funny; why don't they go in the tavern and go to bed?

"If you'll keep your shirt on maybe we will find out. Where are the other four men?

"Oh! they've done gone to bed in the tavern.

"Look through the prairie schooners carefully and tell me what you find?

"What do you expect me to find? You ain't got nothing

193

to do with them damned, all-fired wagons!

"Never mind about that. You don't have to look after the welfare of those men; they're well able to protect themselves. You just go ahead and look in each wagon, one after the other, and tell me what you find.

"In the first one there is some hay, corn and straw, and-

Thereupon the medium slowed down, and, with mouth open wide but tongue stilled, turned his head one way and then another, while his eyes, opened wider than usual, were glued to the crystal.

"Tell me what you see?" commanded Clayton.

"Two iron pots! They are covered with a blanket, and are buried under straw.

"What do you see in the pots?

"Great God! Just look at the gold! And silver, too! Geeminy cracked corn, I don't wonder they have so many shooting irons ready for instant use.

"Look in the next wagon and tell me what you see there.

"Oh there's just some skins of wild animals, some jerked meat, a blanket or two, and some hay and straw.

"Look more carefully. Are you sure there is nothing else in that wagon?

"Well, I should s-a-y not! There's two more pots in that gol-darned wagon.

"Tell me what is in them.

"Silver! Good Lord, I didn't know there was so much silver in one place anywhere in the world. They are filled with silver. And the fellow watching that prairie schooner has just kicked them, I guess to make sure they're still there.

"Isn't there any gold in either of those pots?

"No. God damn it to hell, do you think they'd mix gold and silver. And I just want to warn you, that boss man ain't going to let anybody come near. So you keep away.

"Never mind about that. I just want you to tell me

everything you find in those wagons. Now, go on to the third prairie schooner and look that over carefully.

"Well, I see some more corn and hay—and, I believe, there are some oats. Yes, that's right. And there are some animal skins. I guess that fellow hasn't got a blanket. And he was nodding, too, and his pal in the next wagon told him to wake up and keep his eyes wide open.

"Isn't there anything else in that wagon?

"I don't see anything else.

"Look more carefully, from one end of the wagon to the other.

"Well! well! well! if that don't beat the old scratch! Sure! there's another old iron pot in that wagon, but it was so well covered up that I thought there was just coon skin coats.

"What is in that pot?

"My goodness alive! Ain't there no end to this thing? Why it contains silver, nothing but silver. I wonder what they're going to do with all this gold and silver!

"Go on to the fourth prairie schooner and tell me what you find in it?

"That old fellow is fast asleep, leaning against the top. He better wake up before the boss man in the tavern catches up with him, for I'll be he'd skin him alive.

"Never mind, for the moment, the boss man in the tavern. Do you find anything unusual in that wagon?

"No. Just some hay, and corn, and straw, and skins. Also some camping utensils. And, I believe there's a tent or two in there.

"All right. Now go on to the last wagon. What, if anything of interest, do you find there?

"Just the same kinds of things. More corn and hay and oats. And I see some Indian trinkets, some Indian bows and arrows. That's all.

"All right. Let everything be natural with you for a time.

195

You are at ease. I think you need a rest. We will have some eats before we resume our travel along the old trail."

Thereupon Clayton and I, and the subject, repaired to the other end of the room, and ate what Clayton had prepared for our use before beginning the seance. The boy being at ease, resumed his usual demeanor, rather diffident and retiring, with little to say even when asked a question. When interrogated about what had transpired during the seance, he seemed to recall nothing.

The repast being disposed of, Clayton again hypnotized the subject, handed to him the crystal ball, and the seance was resumed.

"Now, time is passing very fast until you get back to November 1819, and reach Buford's Tavern, fourteen miles east of here, to the east of the Blue Ridge Mountains. Tell me what you find being done about Buford's Tavern?

After a few moments hesitation, the subject said:

"Why, there is the boss man, out there on a horse. And, you bet, he has them saddlebags strapped securely onto the rear of his saddle. One of his pals is leaving the first wagon and coming up to him. He's getting on a horse, too.

"Well, watch them carefully and tell me where they go and what they do.

"There they go, out to the right, over towards the mountain, but to the south.

"How many men are in this party?

"Only two; the boss man, as he seems to me to be, and one of his pals.

"Well, watch them carefully, now, and tell me where they go and what they do?

"They're riding along on an old rutty road, more like a trail than a real road. Now they're leaving the road and following a path up into the edge of the mountain.

"Watch them, and tell me everything they do.

196

"They're back at the tavern. The Negro slave has taken the boss man's horse, also the other man's horse. The boss man and his pal have gone into the tavern, and up to the boss man's room. The boss man is shaking his head.

"Very well, time is fast passing along. Tell me when their next move is made.

"Roosters are crowing. I see the first streaks of dawn resting on the Peaks of Otter. The boss man is lighting his candle. He's now slipping on his trousers, and putting on his boots. He's putting his belt around his waist, and adjusting his pistols. Now he's grabbing up his saddlebags, and is going down the steps of the tavern.

"Watch him carefully. Tell me all that he does.

"Bless my soul, do you know, that Negro slave was out currying and saddling and bridling the boss man's horse. There he is, leading the horse around to the front of the tavern. The boss man is adjusting his saddlebags, and the Negro slave is having trouble to hold the horse, who seems to be prancing to be off. Now the boss man is astride his horse, and is starting off north, to the left of the Peaks of Otter.

"Watch him carefully, and tell me all that he does.

"Well, ain't I doing it? They've gotten off their horses. They're going into a cave. They've candles with them. They've lighted their candles and are examining the cave. They've found some potatoes and other vegetables, and the men shake their heads, as if surprised and disappointed. They're snuffing their candles at the edge of the cave. They're getting on their horses again and are starting back toward the tavern.

"What time is it, if you can judge by the sun?

"Looks like midday. The sun is right overhead. The boss man is looking up at it.

"Well, tell me what they do next, especially when they get back to the tavern. Time is hurrying along.

197

"There he goes, the horse in a fox trot, along the trail which borders Goose Creek and leading to a gap in the Blue Ridge not far from the Twin Peaks. It is on the trail which runs from Bedford County across the mountain to Botetourt County. There's occasionally a house, with a little cleared land around it, but for the most part the hills are covered with forest trees. Now the boss man is leaving the trail, is riding off into the woods, but is shaking his head, as if he doesn't like what he sees; and goes back to the trail again.

"Keep close watch on the boss man, as you term him. Tell me all that he does.

"He's again leaving the trail, crossing a little branch, and going through the woods, up a little hill. Well, isn't that a strange place—a small hill, with a cup-like formation or indentation in it, all covered with giant trees. The boss man is looking around carefully. He's hitched his horse to the limb of a tree, and now is examining the place, as if he's hunting for something. He must like what he has found, for he is smiling. He's knocking the bark off a spot on a big oak tree with the butt of one of his pistols, and now he's cutting the spot more deeply with his hunting knife. He's on his horse again, and is returning toward the tavern.

"Watch him carefully, and tell me anything unusual that he may do. Time is passing faster, and tell me when the boss man reaches the tavern.

"He's done got back to the tavern. The Negro slave's out ready to serve the boss man. The boss man throws him the bridle rein, grabs his saddlebags, and walks into the dining room. Yes, and he's laid his saddlebags carefully under his chair and set his foot on the leather connecting the two bags. He ain't taking no chances with losing them jewels, and I don't blame him.

"Well, time is passing a little faster. Skip over the more unimportant details, and tell me what is done by the boss man and his associates.

198

"It's the next morning. The wagon train is starting off just like it arrived at the tavern, except that the rifles are in the wagons and the horsemen only have their pistols in their belts. They're waving, apparently a good bye, to the tavern keeper.

"Which way are they going?

"The same way the boss man went on his trip horseback the morning before. He's talking to the two men in front, and pointing to the Peaks of Otter.

"Time is speeding along. Tell me where they go.

"They are following the same route the boss man went yesterday morning. There, they're having a little trouble fording the branch. Now they're going along the creek, and have stopped where the boss man went up the little hill. I don't believe the teams can get up the hill. No, they can't. The boss man's pointing and talking. They're carrying the pots up the hill. My! but those pots must be heavy. Now they're carrying picks and shovels up the hill.

"Where are they placing the pots?

"Close by the foot of the giant oak that the boss man chipped bark off of when he was there before. Now they're digging, taking turns at the job.

"Time is passing faster. Tell me what is finally done with the pots.

"You're mighty impatient! Why don't you let me take my time to see and tell you about the whole job?

"We don't care about all the details. We just want to know what was finally done with the pots.

"Well, they've dug a hole about as deep as a man is tall. It's about the size of a grave, except it's wider and rounder. They've hunted up a lot of flat stones and paved the bottom of the hole, and set the pots on the stones, and then covered the pots with more stones. They're filling the hole with the earth taken from it, carefully smoothing over the top, and spreading leaves over the fresh earth.

"Tell me everything they do.

"All of the men have gone back to the wagons, except the boss man. He's cutting a larger place in the side of the tree, a marker I reckon. Well, what a fool! The boss man pulled something like flour out of his pocket and threw it on the freshly cut place. Now the boss man is making some marks on a paper, looks like a sort of diagram. He's done and is joining the other fellows, who had moved down the trail. Now they're on their way back down the creek, the way they came.

"Time is passing faster. Tell me when they stop anywhere.

"They've reached the tavern, and the boss man is talking to the tavern keeper. He seems to be welcomed. The horses are being unhitched.

"Time is passing faster now. Tell me what they do when they make their next move.

"Well, it is next morning, after breakfast. Seven of the men, with the five wagons and two of the saddle horses, are starting off east, along the well traveled road. The boss man and two of his pals, are remaining.

"Time is passing faster now. Watch the three men and tell me if they go anywhere near the buried treasure, or when they take their departure in any direction.

"The boss man and his two pals seem to be sticking around the neighborhood, riding around during the day, and occasionally entering into conversation with the villagers after supper.

"Time is hurrying along. Jump over everything until the boss man, as you term him, or one of his associates, makes a move to leave the tavern.

"It's now the end of about three weeks. The boss man is bidding the tavern keeper good bye. They are on their horses and are heading east."

"Well, that is enough for the present. You may be at rest. We may resume our travels some time later."

Thereupon the subject seemed let down. He resumed his former normal demeanor, diffident and uninterested in anything about him. He was thanked for his visit, and left Magnolia, going in the direction of his home.

My brother, Clayton, and I discussed the seance, not believing anything that had transpired, and, still, wondering if there could be the possibility of some truth in what the subject had blurted forth.

Now, in conclusion:

Not being present at a later seance, when Clayton attempted to get from the subject what had happened to Beale and his 29 associates, I can only state, in a few words, what Clayton told me about it: That, when gazing into the same crystal ball, he asked the subject to follow the party of 10 west, after their second trip to the States, and have them join the 20 left behind to continue searching for gold and silver, and keep with the entire party until, either they returned to their homes or were no more, the subject, in a most realistic but shocked manner, detailed their being set upon by Indians, as they were preparing to leave their operations, when all were killed and scalped.

And thus endeth a weird and almost unbelievable story.

Commentary

If you ask anyone in the environs of Roanoke or Bedford County, Virginia, how much credence can be placed in the story of the Beale Treasure, practically everyone will tell you it is true. Many have studied the codes, some have spent much time and effort trying to decipher them and others, more familiar with the topography, have applied logic to search in likely locations. As interest in the treasure is revived periodically, farmers in the area are plagued with people digging holes in their land.

The focal point for the treasure seekers is the site of the old Buford's Tavern. Only a chimney remains of the old building which is located in the yard next to Locust Level, a brick house built in 1822 by Captain Paschal Buford. Locust Level is part of an original plantation granted to Henry Buford by King George III of England. Henry Buford was a captain in a Virginia Regiment in the American Revolutionary War, High Sheriff, Presiding Justice and prominent in the affairs of Bedford County which was formed in 1754. On his death, Locust Level was the share of his property left to his youngest son, Paschal. Captain Paschal Buford was the owner of the tavern known as Buford's in the stage coach days following the war of 1812-1814 against the British.

The village that grew across the road from the tavern was called Buford's for several years and then known as Buford's Station. Later this was changed to Montvale — more descriptive of the beautiful valley encircled by the Blue

Ridge mountains. This valley extends about eight miles to the north and is drained by the north fork of Goose Creek. The Peaks of Otter rise to four thousand feet above sea level to the east of the upper reaches of the valley. Just west of Montvale is Buford's Gap, a defile about fourteen miles long. Big Lick, located on Ticker's Creek, was at the western end of Buford's Gap.

Big Lick was a stop on the Fincastle stagecoach route, and later on the Lynchburg and Salem Turnpike. After the revolution, Fincastle, the seat of Botetourt county, succeeded New London, in Bedford county, as the center from which the western lands up to the Mississippi were administered. The Fincastle stage coach was quite important in the early days, bringing passengers and mail from the valley of Virginia over the Blue Ridge to Buford's, thence to New London and Lynchburg. The turnpike crossed the Blue Ridge just above Blue Knob at Black Horse Gap where there was a tavern of the same name. This Black Horse Tavern burned down some years ago.

Each trip was an adventure. All types of the region's citizens, gentlemen and yeomen, were met at the taverns. News, political and otherwise was gleaned and proclaimed. A horn blown on a rock near Black Horse Tavern indicated the number of guests Captain Buford could expect to entertain.

The trail of the Fincastle stage is still visible and is negotiable in a jeep. It is used by the Forestry service rangers who keep it open as a fire break in the Jefferson National Forest. The Appalachian Trail passes the Ridge near where the old Black Horse Tavern stood. The south slope of the Blue Ridge in the vicinity is private property, and a chain obstructs entry to the old trail down to Buford.

Jefferson Forest is well named as Thomas Jefferson was revered along its entire length from Monticello, near Charlottesville, to Poplar Forest, his home in Bedford County.

204

Jefferson built Poplar Forest on a four thousand acre tract of land which was left to his wife by her first husband. The house, built of brick, is octagonal in shape. It is landscaped with plantations of boxwood and poplar trees. It is located about a mile south of Forest Depot, eleven miles west of Lynchburg.

It is natural that Thomas Jefferson Beale should have been motivated to live up to the great name given to him and to emulate the spirit of Thomas Jefferson, who had always been interested in exploring the lands to the west. The charter of Virginia, as well as those of Massachusetts, Connecticut and both Carolinas, granted the full extent of land west to the Pacific Ocean. Already a trail was blazed into the west. The great migration of Scots Irish from Pennsylvania, which started before 1750, had populated the valley of Virginia and blazed the way into Tennessee and North Carolina. The route to the borders of southwest Virginia was well established before 1817 and Beale's party could reach it at Salem, seven miles west of Big Lick. Furthermore, the route to Kentucky through the Cumberland Gap, known as the Wilderness Road, pioneered by Daniel Boone, had been used by so many settlers that Kentucky had been admitted to the Union in 1792 and Louisville was already an important frontier town.

It was most likely that Beale took the military route to Vincennes and thence across the Illinois prairies to St. Louis. The famous Santa Fe Trail, which developed later, proved the feasibility of the Beale party's route from St. Louis in 1817. The first trader to open the route for commercial purposes was William Bucknell, who carried $300 worth of goods on pack horses from St. Louis and sold it at an enormous profit in Santa Fe in 1821. While the trail used the Raton Pass, it is likely that Beale did not attempt Raton Pass in December but rather used what was later called the Cimarron cut-off.

The location of gold and silver two hundred and fifty miles north of Santa Fe was confirmed in 1860. Beale's party could have gone eastward from Santa Fe, skirting the Sangre de Cristo mountains around to the northward until they reached the Arkansas river, then going upstream to the vicinity where Salida is now situated. Or they could have proceeded north from Santa Fe up the Rio Grande which is the most likely route.

Although the whole story hangs together extremely well, the reader has the right to ask whether it is true or whether it was concocted after the 1860 gold and silver finds in Colorado became known. Is the Beale treasure a hoax? If so, who perpetrated it?

The writers have found no documentation to prove that Thomas Jefferson Beale ever existed. As far as is known, James P. Ward of Lynchburg is the only person who claims to have seen the originals of Beale's letters to Morriss and the three ciphers. However, none of these facts can be taken as proof that the story is a hoax because many firmly entrenched historical beliefs are based on far less evidence. If anyone fabricated this story, they put a tremendous amount of work into the details. The historical background is accurate and the routes as described above were in use at the time. Even the codes themselves, known as complex substitution ciphers of variable key systems, are of a type used extensively in the time Beale is said to have written them.

When enquiring into the uncertainties and into the characters of those associated with the Beale Papers and the Job Print Pamphlet, one must realize that the setting in which Beale and his party were moving was far different from that in which George Hart wrote his papers or James P. Ward wrote his pamphlet. The Virginia frontier had vanished. The territory of the United States had reached the Pacific in 1848 when Mexico ceded California to the United

States. The heirs to the pioneers had settled in and were developing their holdings and their communities. The residents of the area around Buford's and Big Lick were more interested in local things than the western plains. Yet, the story has the full flavor of the years Beale was making his journeys. Could residents of the Montvale area have enough data to have concocted the tale? What could be their motive? Let us consider the character of the Hart brothers and James P. Ward. Were they reliable men? Were they known for their credibility and honesty? Were they known for their practical jokes?

Clayton Hart was known for his carefulness about money; he was considered miserly and somewhat eccentric. He never married because a wife would be an extravagance. He would walk miles rather than part with train or bus fare, living very simply and wearing his clothes longer than anyone else. He assessed everything according to its monetary value and the fact that he spent 40 years working on the codes and spent his precious money on tools and dynamite, suggests that he believed the story absolutely. He was not known for his sense of humor. The fact that he kept the story to himself and his brother, suggests that he hoped to find the treasure for himself. It is much more likely that someone would make up the story to make a fool of Clayton than the other way round.

Clayton Hart was a shrewd man and not likely to spend 40 years on a tale that did not hold water. He did his best to test it out by going to see James P. Ward and his son. Hart also visited Ward's neighbors to find out what sort of a man he was reputed to be. Clayton obtained a copy of the Job Print pamphlet written by Ward and, in fact, did everything he could to try and prove the story. Therefore the reader may conclude that Clayton believed in the Beale Treasure and did not fabricate the story.

George Hart, senior, Clayton's brother, was a very different man. George was a Virginia gentleman of the old school, distinguished looking and very highly respected in Roanoke and in Washington, D.C. where he moved in 1919. We were privileged to know him for a number of years and we know that he was scrupulously honest and most careful of the truth. George Hart was kindly but straightforward in all his dealings with other people and all who knew him will tell that he would not deceive anyone or knowingly mislead them.

In an attempt to set forth the story of the Beale Treasure as clearly as he could, George Hart senior wrote an essay describing all that is known or surmised concerning the Beale treasure in 1952, a copy of which is found in this book.

A sister of Clayton and George retained Clayton's papers when he died. This sister was always closer to Clayton than to George, being of a similar temperament. Clayton was concentrating on the Indian burial mounds which are close to Buford's Tavern but he had little more to show for his 40 years of work than had George or any of those who had been searching for the treasure since the Job Print Pamphlet came out.

James P. Ward is another matter. All we know of him comes from his pamphlet and from Clayton's description and that of his neighbors. Clayton Hart seemed satisfied that Ward's story was true and not made up. Clayton's belief in Ward's story was reinforced when he went back and questioned Ward's neighbors and was told by them that Ward was a man of his word and well thought of in his community. However, even with all this, there is really nothing to prove Ward's story. What became of the box containing the original letters and ciphers? Was this lost in the fire at the Job Print Press? Was it given to Ward's son? Or did Ward keep it himself? It seems strange that the Hart brothers did not question the absence of the original papers or that Ward said nothing about their disposition in the pamphlet. On the other hand Ward may have kept the originals himself, as is usually done by any writer, and simply given copies to the printer. We have been unable to trace any descendants of James P. Ward and his son, so we have not been able to find out whether they have the box and its contents.

Although James P. Ward could have fabricated the tale, the fact that he lived very simply and his circumstances deteriorated steadily as time went on seem to bear out the truth of his story that he wasted years of his life on the Beale treasure and allowed his business and family to suffer. However, the famous code breaker, Colonel Fabyan, wrote to George Hart, "Now, in reference to the three ciphers; it seems improbable to us that a cipher of this character could be deciphered by a novice without a key, regardless of whether he put twenty years or forty years on it. . . . The stumbling of a novice upon a method of this character lies rather beyond the range of possibility, and the conviction follows that they, Ward and son, were in possession of the key of not only No. 2, but also of No. 1 and No. 3, with the result that the treasure referred to has long since been removed and converted." From this passage it is obvious that Colonel Fabyan thought that Ward or some member of his family had found the treasure, but if this were so, surely they would have used the money for some comforts in life. Such an enormous amount of wealth could not remain forever hidden by the family. Someone would have let out the secret. No one could resist wearing a jewel or spending a little of the gold. The fact that the Wards lived in poverty brings us to the conclusion that they did not fabricate the story but believed it to their own misfortune and never found the treasure.

Another question that is often asked is: Did Colonel Fabyan find the treasure? He was an incredibly successful breaker of codes and the Harts never heard from him again. Was this because he was successful in deciphering the codes and wanted to get the treasure for himself, or because he was unsuccessful and did not want to admit defeat? We do not know.

Some people have suggested that Edgar Allan Poe's tale, "The Gold Bug," was based on the Beale treasure story, but as the code used in "The Gold Bug" is quite a different type, there seems no reason to link the two. It is a well known fact that Poe was haunted by bitter poverty all his life so he could not have found the treasure.

Was it possible that any members of Beale's party came back and dug up the treasure? Yes, it is. Since they knew where it was hidden they would have had no need to go to Robert Morriss for the box and, if they took more than their fair share, they wouldn't want to let anyone know it had been moved.

Is it possible that the treasure is still there if the story is true? Who can say? It would be difficult to get that amount of metal out of the area without being discovered nowadays, but it would have been much easier when the Blue Ridge and environs was less populated. We believe the story is true and we will continue to try to decipher the codes and search for the treasure until there is evidence to prove otherwise.

What is the value of the Hart papers? This manuscript is valuable because it was written by a man of integrity who had been in contact with people who had known James P. Ward and his son. George Hart had read the Job Print Pamphlet and vouched for its existence. Also he had spent as many years on the mystery as had James P. Ward.

The account of the seance and the hypnotizing of the boy, Lloyd Cunning, which appears in the Hart papers, is of doubtful value. Some of the terms used belong to a different date from Beale's day. Dates and descriptions do not agree with the contents of the deciphered paper No. 2. For instance, Beale in his letter to Morriss, and Ward in the pamphlet, refer to Beale's arriving in Lynchburg in January 1820 after being in Buford for a month; therefore Beale must have arrived in Buford in December 1819, not November as the Hart manuscript states. Also Lloyd Cunning, the boy under hypnosis, describes seeing jewels in the first deposit of treasure in 1819, but according to paper no. 2, these were not brought until the second trip in 1822. The term 'prairie schooner' was not in use until after 1825, yet the boy uses this term several times.

However, this account does not affect the veracity of the rest of the Hart story.

In summing up the results of this study, I would say that there is a higher probability that the story is true than that it is a hoax. This being so, there is a strong possibility that the treasure is still there. However, the only way we can be sure is to decipher the remaining papers, find the vault and see for ourselves. Meanwhile I believe that the background given in this book and the sharing of data will be of tremendous help to all those trying to solve this mystery.

The following quote from Colonel Fabyan's letter to George Hart, senior bears this out.

"I repeat, that the problem has my interest, and I am writing in the vain hope that either you or Clayton I. Hart can give us further information, because the psychology of it is about all we have to go on in picking out our point of attack. In the meantime we will retain the pamphlet, and work on it as we can find time to do so."

Appendix

Treasure Hunting Information

Before digging for treasure it is well to find out whether the property is privately owned or part of public lands. If you want to dig on private property be sure to ask permission of the owner. Agree to split with him if you find anything and be sure to get any such arrangement in writing as the owner of the land can claim the treasure. Local landowners in the Beale Treasure area are fed up with holes being dug on their land and left unfilled where cattle and humans could fall in and break a limb. You may be chased off with buckshot if you dig without permission.

If you wish to dig on public land, permission should be asked of the Department of the Interior.

Should you be successful in deciphering papers No. 1 and 3 and finding out the exact location of the vault, you should buy the land if it is privately owned and obtain the mineral rights if it is on public land in order to safeguard yourself.

A Statement put out by the Treasury Department B.M. 62-20 which gives information regarding the acquisition and possession of gold and treasure, is reprinted below for your benefit.

You will be glad to know that there are no laws on the United States government books which make it possible to take treasure away from you. The same is true in most states but some such as Florida, collect a percentage of the treasure.

Useful Equipment

A treasure hunter's needs vary with the type of treasure he is hunting and the type of countryside where it is hidden. There are various good Treasure Hunting manuals which give extensive information, but for hunting the Beale Treasure you might be interested in the items we have found useful in our own searches.

Transportation
A station wagon to carry tools and baggage and to sleep in if necessary.

Maps and Compasses
The maps supplied in this book are accurate and probably all you will need. If you want others, they can be obtained from the Coastal and Geodetic Survey Department, Washington, D.C. The Government Printing Office issues a free catalogue from which the map you want can be selected. A list of Aeronautical Section Charts also can be obtained from this office and these provide a bird's-eye view of the land and show magnetic variation.

You will need a good compass so you can get your bearings. Also a surveyor's tape to measure distances.

Detectors
A metal detector or electronic treasure finder is of great help in searching for treasure. There are two basic designs, one sends out a balanced electromagnetic field; the other a radio signal which is picked up by a radio receiver. Either carries an audible tone.

214

No metal detector can distinguish one metal from another. They react to beer cans, nails, or any metallic object, so there is no guarantee that you will find treasure when they react. However, each metal has a slightly different sound and the experienced user can recognize the different tones.

The radio signal design is not so sensitive as the electromagnetic model, but it has the greatest depth range. It can respond to large metal objects 30 feet underground. Each model comes with complete instructions for use. About a dozen companies make detectors in this country and their price ranges from $60 to $1,000. It is also possible to make your own and the Treasure Hunter's Manual gives instructions for this.

In most towns it is possible to rent a metal detector if you do not want to go to the expense of buying one.

Tools

We take spades, a pickaxe, a hunting knife, a flashlight and matches whenever we go. These items cover most contingencies and if you take the G.I. type of spade it is not so heavy to carry as the long-handled type.

First Aid Kit

Any of the neatly boxed first aid kits are good, but be sure they contain a snakebite kit and carry plenty of insect repellent as there are always insects in this area.

Do Not Go Treasure Hunting Alone in isolated areas. Parts of the Blue Ridge are lonely and the going is rough. Should you fall or meet with any kind of accident you would have to wait a long time to get help. Should you find the treasure you will need help marking the spot and watching over it while other arrangements are made. Unless you are an experienced explorer, take a companion along. This area is very beautiful and has many interesting wild flowers and birds as well as the Beale Treasure, so you should have no difficulty in finding companions even if they say they are not interested in treasure hunting; there are plenty of other things to do. There are several good places to eat and to stay. The Hotel Roanoke in Roanoke is first-class and open all the year round, then there is the Peaks of Otter Lodge open from April to October. We like this best because the food is good and it is close to the treasure area. The Bedford Motel is also good and close to Goose Creek. You will come across several others that give good service but we do not know them personally.

A Statement from the Office of Director of the Mint, Treasury Department, Washington, D.C. pertaining to buried treasure.

The Treasury Department has no authentic information with regard to lost or buried treasure. A number of letters concerning local treasure legends, which abound in all parts of the country, are in the Department's files but none has been verified. However, you might be interested in the legal requirements with which the Treasury is concerned that might be applicable in the event of a discovery of such a treasure.

It is not necessary to obtain a license from the Treasury Department in order to search for buried treasure. If the search is to be conducted on public lands, however, permission of the Department of Interior may be required; and, if the search is to be made on private property, arrangements would, of course, be made with the owner.

With regard to gold contained in buried treasure, the acquisition, possession and use of gold in the United States is governed by the Gold Regulations. In general, gold may be acquired and held within the United States only by persons who are regularly engaged in an industry, profession or art in which gold is required for legitimate and customary use as authorized by the Gold Regulations. Section 54.20 of the Regulations permits the acquisition and possession in the United States of gold coins of recognized special value to collectors of rare and unusual coin, including all gold coins made prior to April 5, 1933.

Pursuant to orders issued in 1933, gold bullion in the United States on that date was required to be delivered to the Treasury Department for redemption at bullion value. Any gold which should have been delivered pursuant to such orders, is now required to be delivered for redemption at the rate of $20.67 per fine troy ounce subject to certain rights reserved to the Government to assess penalties for violation of the orders.

With regard to silver contained in buried treasure, a Treasury license is not required to hold or sell silver bullion or coins. Silver coins issued by the United States are, of course, legal tender in the United States.

In view of the foregoing, when any gold is found in this country by any person, the fact should be reported promptly to the Director, Office of Domestic Gold and Silver Operations, Treasury Department, Washington 25, D.C., with complete details, including a description of the gold and a statement of the circumstances under which it was found, in order that specific instructions may be given.

In the absence of complete facts, it would be impossible to determine what further interest the United States Government might have in buried treasure. With regard to the Federal tax applicable, the Internal Revenue Service has indicated that the value of buried treasure discovered by an individual, the owner being unknown, will constitute taxable income to the person who discovers it for the taxable year in which he reduces it to his possession under a claim of ownership. Further information as to the application of the Federal tax laws in the case of buried treasure may be obtained from your local United States Internal Revenue Office or by writing to the Internal Revenue Service, Washington 25, D.C., giving complete details.

This statement is issued for general information. It does not have the effect of law, regulation or ruling.

Some Further Notes on Codes

Thomas Jefferson established a cipher which he gave to Lewis and Clark to use when they corresponded with him, but they did not need it. A copy is given here and the original with notes on its use can be found in the Jefferson documents in the Library of Congress. The key to this cipher is ARTICHOKES.

	a	b	c	d	e	f	g	h	i	j	k	l	m	n	o	p	q	r	s	t	u	v	w	x	y	z
a	b	c	d	e	f	g	h	i	j	k	l	m	n	o	p	q	r	s	t	u	v	w	x	y	z	&
b	c	d	e	f	g	h	i	j	k	l	m	n	o	p	q	r	s	t	u	v	w	x	y	z	&	a
c	d	e	f	g	h	i	j	k	l	m	n	o	p	q	r	s	t	u	v	w	x	y	z	&	a	b
d	e	f	g	h	i	j	k	l	m	n	o	p	q	r	s	t	u	v	w	x	y	z	&	a	b	c
e	f	g	h	i	j	k	l	m	n	o	p	q	r	s	t	u	v	w	x	y	z	&	a	b	c	d
f	g	h	i	j	k	l	m	n	o	p	q	r	s	t	u	v	w	x	y	z	&	a	b	c	d	e
g	h	i	j	k	l	m	n	o	p	q	r	s	t	u	v	w	x	y	z	&	a	b	c	d	e	f
h	i	j	k	l	m	n	o	p	q	r	s	t	u	v	w	x	y	z	&	a	b	c	d	e	f	g
i	j	k	l	m	n	o	p	q	r	s	t	u	v	w	x	y	z	&	a	b	c	d	e	f	g	h
j	k	l	m	n	o	p	q	r	s	t	u	v	w	x	y	z	&	a	b	c	d	e	f	g	h	i
k	l	m	n	o	p	q	r	s	t	u	v	w	x	y	z	&	a	b	c	d	e	f	g	h	i	j
l	m	n	o	p	q	r	s	t	u	v	w	x	y	z	&	a	b	c	d	e	f	g	h	i	j	k
m	n	o	p	q	r	s	t	u	v	w	x	y	z	&	a	b	c	d	e	f	g	h	i	j	k	l
n	o	p	q	r	s	t	u	v	w	x	y	z	&	a	b	c	d	e	f	g	h	i	j	k	l	m
o	p	q	r	s	t	u	v	w	x	y	z	&	a	b	c	d	e	f	g	h	i	j	k	l	m	n
p	q	r	s	t	u	v	w	x	y	z	&	a	b	c	d	e	f	g	h	i	j	k	l	m	n	o
q	r	s	t	u	v	w	x	y	z	&	a	b	c	d	e	f	g	h	i	j	k	l	m	n	o	p
r	s	t	u	v	w	x	y	z	&	a	b	c	d	e	f	g	h	i	j	k	l	m	n	o	p	q
s	t	u	v	w	x	y	z	&	a	b	c	d	e	f	g	h	i	j	k	l	m	n	o	p	q	r
t	u	v	w	x	y	z	&	a	b	c	d	e	f	g	h	i	j	k	l	m	n	o	p	q	r	s
u	v	w	x	y	z	&	a	b	c	d	e	f	g	h	i	j	k	l	m	n	o	p	q	r	s	t
v	w	x	y	z	&	a	b	c	d	e	f	g	h	i	j	k	l	m	n	o	p	q	r	s	t	u
w	x	y	z	&	a	b	c	d	e	f	g	h	i	j	k	l	m	n	o	p	q	r	s	t	u	v
x	y	z	&	a	b	c	d	e	f	g	h	i	j	k	l	m	n	o	p	q	r	s	t	u	v	w
y	z	&	a	b	c	d	e	f	g	h	i	j	k	l	m	n	o	p	q	r	s	t	u	v	w	x
z	&	a	b	c	d	e	f	g	h	i	j	k	l	m	n	o	p	q	r	s	t	u	v	w	x	y
&	a	b	c	d	e	f	g	h	i	j	k	l	m	n	o	p	q	r	s	t	u	v	w	x	y	z

Jefferson also invented a cipher system which is still in use today. Thomas Jefferson was in contact with Dr. Robert Patterson of the University of Pennsylvania at the time and they had much correspondence on this wheel cipher. Details

219

of this can be found in the documents in the Library of Congress.

It is believed by some people that Thomas Jefferson Beale was a third degree Mason of the Scottish rite and the secret of the codes can only be discovered by another Mason, because Beale and his party wanted to safeguard their families and a brother Mason would see that this was done. One of the codes used by the Masons of Virginia in Thomas Jefferson Beale's time was as follows:

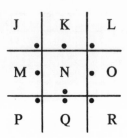

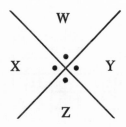

As an example of the use of this, BLUE RIDGE would appear as

Below is some work on the code done by a man now deceased. It was sent to us without any note regarding the document he used as a key.

71-194-38-1701-89-76-11-83-1629-48-94-63-132-16-111-
(L E   E) (B   R O K E N)   (B O N E   S) —
95-84-341-975-14-40-64-27-81-139-213-63-90-1120-8-
(G R   A   V   E) (S L A B) (R   O   U   N D)   (-)
15-3-126-2018-40-74-758-485-604-230-436-664-582-150-
(T UR   N   S) (E A   S   T) (R   O   L   L) (-)
251-284-308-231-124-211-486-225-401-370-11-101-305-139-
(H   O   L   E) (T   U   R N) (S   O   U   T H) (-)
189-17-33-88-208-193-145-1-94-73-416-918-263-28-500-
(R O P E) (G L   O   VE) (B E   L   O   W (-)
538-356-117-136-219-27-176-130-10-460-25-485-18-436-65-
(O N) (R   O   O   F) (N   O   T) (B A S   E) (-)   (-)
84-200-283-118-320-138-36-416-280-15-71-224-961-44-16-
(L A   N   K) (H O   I   S   T)   (T H E   R   E) (-)
401-39-88-61-304-12-21-24-283-134-92-63-246-486
(N E A R) (O   N E) (T W O)   (F I   V   E)
682-7- 219-184-360-780-18-64-463-474-131-160-79-73-440-
(M A K   E)   (A) (N   E T) (H E   A   V   Y) (T O)
95-18-64-581-34-69-123-367-460-17-81-12-103-880-62-
(G E T) (M E N) (T   O) (H   E   L P) (Y   O   U)
116-97-103-862-70-60-1317-471-540-208-121-890-346-36
(L I   F   T)   (P A R   T) (T I   E) (B A   R)

Below is a photostat of the only piece of paper believed to be from the iron box in existence today. This appears to be a page torn from a book and we have spent many hours trying to trace the type of book from which it might have been torn. We have been unable to find any use for the few numbers which appear on the paper and have come to the conclusion that it was used as scrap paper by either Beale or Morriss. Yet, why should it have been preserved? If it is really from the iron box why was it separated from the others?

The paper is definitely old. It was given to us by a family in Roanoke who wish to remain anonymous to avoid harrassment. This family says the paper has been handed down and has always been considered one of the Beale Treasure papers from the iron box.

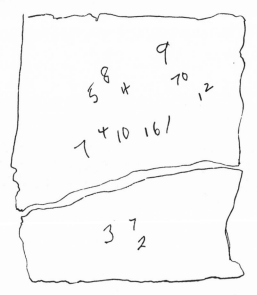

Some New Notes on the Codes—
Discussion of Job Print Pamphlet

Since *Gold in the Blue Ridge* was first published, the authors have been steadily working on the codes and researching the story. Some of the results of this work are given in the following chapters together with material supplied by others who are in contact with us. Page 6   gives the result of a computer run which appeared promising. Page 222 shows two of the pieces of paper from the box as it is thought the numbers might be helpful with the codes. Although someone said there were receipts in the box with the letters, the Job Print Pamphlet and the Hart papers describe them as 'worthless pieces of paper'.

Three of the most famous American codebreakers have worked on the Beale Treasure codes without success.

HERBERT O. YARDLEY of M1–8, who founded the American Black Chamber and wrote the controversial book of this same name, was perhaps the best known. Yardley was sent a typed copy of the pamphlet by Jos. McGehee of Roanoke, Va., in 1931. Yardley in turn sent a copy to H. E. Langren, editor of the Cryptogram in July 1954. This was published in December 1954.

COLONEL FABYAN of the Riverbank Laboratories Illinois, to whom George Hart Sr. sent a copy of the Job Print pamphlet in 1925, was a wealthy merchant who maintained research labs on genetics and cryptology on his large estate in Illinois. Fabyan's first interest in cryptology was trying to prove that Bacon wrote Shakespeare! In World War I, when America declared war, Fabyan gathered around him a group of codebreakers of such talent that Riverbank became famous worldwide for its code-breaking.

WILLIAM FREIDMAN, born in Russia and brought to this country as a child, was the most brilliant cryptologist this country has had to date. He was hired by Fabyan and became head of the Department of Cyphers at Riverbank. In addition to his work as cryptanalyst, Friedman was responsible for teaching groups of Army Intelligence officers sent to learn cryptology. All these men were defeated by the Beale Treasure codes and, in spite of the fact that the codes are still given to training classes of Army Intelligence officers, they remain unbroken.

WHY?

One reason is that they are irregular substitution cyphers and this type is the most difficult to break without the key. As Colonel Fabyan wrote to George Hart, 'it is unlikely that anyone could have deciphered one of the codes without a knowledge of the key.' This is why the question was asked about Robert Morriss on page 244 If a person has some inkling of the key, a child could decipher the codes.

One day someone will hit on the right document and confound all the experts.

Another reason why the codes are still unbroken is that most people do not have the correct set of numbers and are not using the copy of the Declaration of Independence that Beale used. This brings us to the differences between the Marshall Library copy of the Job Print Pamphlet and the Hart papers and this book. But first we should ask

ARE THEY REAL CODES OR
JUST A JUMBLE OF NUMBERS?

Colonel Fabyan in his letter to George Hart said he thought they were real codes.

H. O. Yardley believed they were authentic.

Richard Helms of the C.I.A. wrote that 'he was not positively prepared to say they were a hoax.' See letter, page 7.

Most computer analysts who have worked on the codes in recent years consider they are genuine codes.

Per Holst of Massachusetts made a computer study and found that the patterns inherent in the cryptographers' selection of cyphers show distinct characteristics and a clear relationship between the three.

Having accepted the codes as authentic, let us move on to the discussion of them and the variations between the Marshall Job Print Pamphlet and Hart versions of codes and the Declaration of Independence.

As mentioned on page 237 it is most important to remember that Beale refers to the SHEETS of paper he put in the box. Morriss also refers to SHEETS of paper when he gave the box to Ward. Ward in turn speaks of SHEETS of paper and Hazelwood brought SHEETS of paper to Clayton Hart from Ward. Hazelwood said that Ward altered the codes so others could not find the treasure.

This would explain the differences between the two versions and make it almost certain that what Clayton copied and gave to George Hart was the correct version of the original codes, and that the Declaration given in this book and in the Hart papers is the one used by Beale. Incidentally, this is the official version used by the original signers of the Declaration of Independence.

The above versions appeared in the *Argosy* article of August 1954 which P. B. Innis wrote. They also appear where ever other writers have copied from the Innis writings or the Hart papers.

Versions earlier than the Innis article mostly use the Job Print Pamphlet version because this was what was leaked out around Roanoke, Virginia. The copy of the Job Print Pamphlet which is in the Marshall, Virginia, Library Freidman papers, is believed to be the one Clayton Hart obtained from Ward and gave to George and which George sent to Colonel Fabyan. It is most likely that Freidman got it from Fabyan and worked on it while at Riverbank.

Hazelwood had told Clayton Hart that Ward changed the

numbers in the pamphlet to prevent people finding the treasure which rightfully belonged to the descendants of Beale's party. If Ward did this, then the pamphlets are the source of the altered codes and different version of the Declaration and partly explain why the codes have not been deciphered.

The copy of the codes Joseph McGehee sent to H. O. Yardley contained exactly the same numbers as the pamphlet in the Marshall Library. Articles about the treasure written by Hiram Herbert and others who lived in the Roanoke area, also contain the same numbers as the Marshall Job Print Pamphlet.

The copy of the codes H. O. Yardley sent to the editor of the Cryptogram which was published in December 1954, contains exactly the same numbers as the pamphlet.

Clayton and George very carefully kept the copy of the codes they got from Hazelwood to themselves. When George Hart typed up the copy of 'all that is known and surmised of the Beale treasure' to put in the Roanoke Library, he used a copy of the written text he had made years before from the pamphlet, and copied the codes from Clayton's notes and the Declaration from the official version.

Therefore it appears that Freidman, Yardley, Fabyan and many others have been working with the altered codes and the wrong Declaration.

Of course, most copies of the codes contain typographical errors to a greater or lesser degree. It is difficult to copy pages of numbers without a mistake. For instance, we get a typo of 37 instead of 87. Such as these are easy to spot and easily corrected, but the variations in the Marshall Job Print Pamphlet have differences that cannot be simple typos.

To make it easy to compare them, copies of both versions of code number 2 are given. If you check out the other two codes you will see differences there also. Not so many, of course, but enough to make a difference in deciphering.

The Declaration shown in the pamphlet is not only very

strangely numbered but has many differences in wording. It is not a known variation of the official version used by Jefferson. The pamphlet Declaration is given below and the official Declaration is given on page 158 .

The word differences and differences in spelling are very important. The pamphlet Declaration has a number of word differences and spelling changes which would affect deciphering. To mention a few:

page 17. line 8, *i*nalienable, Hart version *u*nalienable

line 13, to institute *a* new government. Extra word 'a'

line 18, 'now' disposed, instead of 'more' disposed

page 19. line 6, 'powers' of government instead of 'Forms'

The numbering of the pamphlet Declaration should be considered carefully. It is unlikely that the mistakes are accidental. The irregularities are too regular. Also to number to 480 and then to continue to number to 480 again, would surely have been noticed and corrected as the encipherer went over the paper. These numbers are probably the efforts of one or more of the many decoders who handled the pamphlet and used it as a work sheet. It is unlikely that Beale himself numbered the Declaration this way and left a record for everyone to see.

The numbers written on the pamphlet Declaration are not as important as the word changes in the Declaration itself.

Could this be the copy Beale used?

It is possible, but it is most likely that Beale used the official version. Even so, it is well worth trying the pamphlet Declaration, correctly numbered, as a key to the undeciphered codes.

The 3 codes from the Job Print Pamphlet photocopies
in the Library of the George C. Marshall Foundation
Lexington, Virginia .   There are many differences
between these and the codes given in the Innis writings
and in George Hart's version.   See text.

no 1. Location of the Vault.

1 71,194,38,1701,89,76,11,83,1629,48,94,63,132,16,111,95,84,341,
2 975,14,40,64,27,81,139,213,63,90,1120,8,15,3,126,2018,40,74,
3 758,485,604,230,436,664,582,150,251,284,308,231,124,211,486,225,
4 401,370,11,101,305,139,189,17,33,88,208,193,145,1,94,73,416,
5 918,263,28,500,538,356,117,136,219,27,176,130,10,460,25,485,18,
436,65,84,283,118,320,138,36,416,280,15,71,224,961,44,16,401,
39,88,61,304,12,21,24,283,134,92,63,246,486,682,7,219,184,360,780,
18,64,463,474,131,160,79,73,440,95,18,64,581,34,69,128,367,460,17,
81,12,103,820,62,116,97,103,862,70,60,1317,471,540,208,121,890,
346,36,150,50,56,614,13,120,63,219,812,2160,1730,99,35,18,21,136,
872,15,28,170,88,4,30,44,112,18,147,436,195,320,37,122,113,6,140,
8,120,305,42,58,461,44,106,301,13,408,680,93,86,116,530,82,568,9,
102,38,416,99,71,216,728,965,818,2,39,121,195,14,326,148,234,18,
55,131,234,361,824,5,81,823,48,961,10,26,33,10,1101,365,92,88,181,
275,346,201,206,86,212,324,820,940,64,326,18,48,122,85,216,284,
919,861,326,985,233,64,68,232,431,960,50,29,31,216,521,603,14,612,
81,360,36,51,62,194,73,60,200,314,676,112,4,28,18,61,136,247,819,
921,1060,464,995,10,6,66,119,38,41,49,602,423,962,302,294,875,78,
14,23,111,109,62,31,501,823,216,280,34,24,150,1000,162,286,19,21,
17,340,19,242,31,86,234,140,607,115,33,191,67,104,86,52,88,16,80,
121,67,95,122,216,548,96,11,201,77,364,218,65,667,830,236,154,211,
10,98,34,119,56,216,119,71,218,1164,1496,1817,51,39,210,36,3,19,
540,332,22,141,617,84,290,80,46,207,411,150,29,38,46,172,85,194,
39,261,543,897,624,13,212,416,127,231,19,4,63,96,12,101,418,16,140
230,460,538,19,27,88,612,1431,90,716,275,74,83,11,426,89,72,84,
1300,1706,814,221,132,40,102,34,868,975,1101,84,16,79,23,16,81,122
324,403,212,227,236,447,55,86,34,43,212,107,96,314,264,1065,323
428,501,203,124,95,216,814,2906,954,820,2,301,112, 176,213,71,37,9
202,35,10,2,41,17,84,221,736,826,214,11,60,760.

228

115, 73, 24, 807, 37, 52, 49, 17, 31, 62, 647, 22, 7, 15, 140, 47, 29, 107, 79, 84,
56, 239, 10, 26, 811, 5, 196, 308, 83, 52, 160, 136, 59, 211, 36, 9, 46, 316, 554,
122, 106, 95, 53, 58, 2, 42, 7, 35, 122, 53, 31, 82, 77, 250, 196, 56, 96, 118, 71,
140, 287, 28, 353, 37, 1005, 65, 147, 807, 24, 3, 8, 12, 47, 43, 59, 807, 45, 316,
101, 41, 78, 154, 1005, 122, 138, 191, 16, 77, 49, 102, 57, 72, 34, 73, 85, 35, 371,
59, 196, 81, 92, 191, 106, 273, 60, 394, 620, 270, 220, 106, 388, 287, 63, 3, 6,
191, 122, 43, 234, 400, 106, 290, 314, 47, 48, 81, 96, 26, 115, 92, 158, 191, 110,
77, 85, 197, 46, 10, 113, 140, 353, 48, 120, 106, 2, 607, 61, 420, 811, 29, 125, 14,
20, 37, 105, 28, 248, 16, 159, 7, 35, 19, 301, 125, 110, 486, 287, 98, 117, 511, 62,
51, 220, 37, 113, 140, 807, 138, 540, 6, 44, 287, 388, 117, 18, 79, 344, 34, 20, 59,
511, 548, 107, 603, 220, 7, 66, 154, 41, 20, 50, 6, 575, 122, 154, 248, 110, 61, 52, 33,
30, 5, 38, 8, 14, 84, 57, 540, 217, 115, 71, 28, 84, 63, 43, 131, 29, 138, 47, 73, 239,
540, 52, 53, 79, 118, 51, 44, 63, 196, 12, 225, 112, 3, 49, 79, 353, 105, 56, 371, 557,
211, 505, 125, 360, 133, 143, 101, 15, 26, 1, 540, 62, 14, 205, 140, 344, 26, 811, 138,
115, 48, 73, 34, 205, 316, 607, 63, 220, 7, 52, 150, 44, 52, 16, 40, 37, 158, 807, 37,
121, 12, 95, 10, 15, 35, 12, 131, 62, 115, 102, 807, 49, 53, 135, 138, 30, 31, 62, 67, 41,
85, 63, 10, 106, 807, 138, 8, 113, 20, 52, 33, 37, 353, 287, 140, 47, 85, 50, 37, 49, 47,
64, 6, 7, 71, 33, 4, 43, 47, 63, 1, 27, 600, 208, 230, 15, 191, 246, 85, 94, 511, 2, 270,
20, 39, 7, 33, 44, 22, 49, 7, 10, 3, 811, 164, 44, 486, 230, 353, 211, 200, 31, 10, 38,
140, 297, 61, 603, 320, 302, 606, 287, 2, 44, 33, 32, 511, 548, 10, 6, 250, 557, 246,
53, 37, 52, 83, 47, 320, 38, 33, 807, 7, 44, 30, 31, 250, 10, 15, 35, 106, 160, 113, 31,
102, 406, 230, 540, 320, 20, 66, 33, 101, 807, 138, 301, 316, 353, 320, 220, 37, 52,
28, 540, 320, 33, 8, 48, 107, 50, 811, 7, 2, 113, 73, 16, 125, 11, 110, 67, 102, 807, 33,
59, 81, 158, 38, 43, 581, 138, 19, 85, 400, 38, 43, 77, 14, 27, 8, 47, 138, 63, 140, 44,
85, 22, 177, 106, 250, 311, 217, 2, 10, 7, 1005, 4, 20, 25, 44, 48, 7, 26, 46, 110, 230,
807, 191, 84, 112, 147, 44, 110, 121, 125, 96, 41, 51, 50, 140, 56, 47, 152, 540,
63, 807, 28, 42, 250, 138, 582, 98, 643, 32, 107, 140, 112, 26, 85, 138, 540, 53, 20,
125, 371, 38, 36, 10, 52, 118, 136, 102, 420, 150, 112, 71, 14, 20, 7, 24, 18, 12, 807,
37, 67, 110, 62, 33, 21, 95, 220, 511, 102, 811, 30, 83, 84, 305, 620, 15, 2, 108, 220,
106, 353, 105, 106, 60, 275, 72, 8, 50, 205, 185, 112, 125, 540, 65, 106, 807, 188, 96, 110,
16, 73, 33, 807, 150, 409, 400, 50, 154, 285, 96, 106, 316, 270, 205, 101, 811, 400, 8,
44, 37, 52, 40, 241, 34, 205, 38, 16, 46, 47, 85, 24, 44, 15, 64, 73, 138, 807, 85, 78, 110,
33, 420, 505, 53, 37, 38, 22, 31, 10, 110, 106, 101, 140, 15, 38, 3, 5, 44, 7, 98, 287,
185, 150, 96, 33, 84, 125, 807, 191, 96, 311, 111, 118, 410, 370, 643, 466, 106, 41, 107,
603, 230, 275, 30, 150, 105, 49, 53, 287, 250, 208, 134, 7, 53, 12, 47, 85, 63, 138, 110,
21, 112, 140, 485, 485, 505, 14, 73, 84, 575, 1005, 150, 200, 16, 42, 5, 4, 25, 42,
8, 16, 811, 125, 160, 32, 205, 603, 807, 81, 96, 405, 41, 600, 136, 14, 20, 28, 26,
353, 302, 246, 8, 131, 160, 140, 84, 440, 42, 16, 811, 40, 67, 101, 102, 194, 138,
205, 51, 63, 241, 540, 122, 8, 10, 63, 180, 47, 48, 140, 288.

```
317,8,92,73,112,89,67,319,29,96,107,41,631,78,146,397,118,98,
114,246,348,116,74,89,12,65,32,14,91,19,76,121,216,85,33,66,15,
109,68,77,43,24,122,96,119,36,211,201,15,44,11,46,89,18,136,68,
317,28,90,32,304,71,43,221,129,176,310,313,81,99,264,380,56,37,
319,2,44,53,28,44,75,98,102,37,95,107,117,64,99,136,48,154,99,175,
```

1 89,315,326,79,96,214,218,311,43,99,51,90,75,129,96,33,28,103,84,
2 65,26,41,246,84,279,98,116,32,59,74,66,69,240,15,8,121,20,77,89,
3 31,11,106,81,191,224,329,18,75,52,82,117,201,39,23,217,27,21,84,
4 35,54,109,128,49,77,89,1,91,217,94,55,83,116,251,269,311,96,54,32,
5 120,18,132,102,219,211,84,159,219,275,312,64,10,106,87,75,47,21,
6 29,37,81,44,18,126,115,132,169,191,203,76,81,299,314,337,351,96,11
7 28,97,313,329,106,24,93,3,19,17,26,60,73,88,14,126,138,234,286,
8 297,321,365,264,19,22,84,56,107,98,123,111,214,136,7,33,45,40,13,
9 28,46,42,107,196,227,344,198,203,247,116,19,8,212,230,31,6,328,
10 65,48,52,59,41,122,33,117,11,19,25,71,36,45,83,76,89,92,31,65,70
11 83,96,27,33,44,50,61,24,112,130,149,176,180,194,143,171,205,296,
12 87,19,44,51,89,98,34,41,208,173,66,9,16,25,8,113,175,90,56,
13 203,19,177,193,206,157,200,219,260,291,305,618,951,320,18,124,78,
14 65,19,32,124,48,53,57,84,96,207,244,66,82,119,71,11,86,77,213,54,
15 82,316,245,303,86,97,106,212,18,37,15,81,89,16,7,81,39,96,14,43,
16 216,118,29,55,199,136,172,213,64,8,227,304,811,221,364,819,375,
17 128,296,1,18,53,76,10,15,23,19,71,84,120,134,66,73,89,96,230,48,
18 77,26,101,127,236,219,439,179,171,61,226,313,215,102,18,167,262,
   114,218,66,59,43,27,19,13,92,48,62,119,34,127,139,34,128,129,74,
   63,120,11,54,61,73,92,190,66,75,191,124,265,89,96,126,274,896,917,
   434,461,235,890,312,413,329,391,96,105,217,86,118,22,77,64,42,12,
   7,55,24,93,67,97,199,121,135,181,203,219,228,256,21,34,77,319,374,
   382,673,684,717,864,219,4,19,92,16,63,92,22,46,55,69,74,112,134,
   186,175,119,213,419,312,343,264,119,186,219,343,417,845,951,124,
   209,49,617,856,924,936,72,19,28,11,35,42,40,66,85,94,112,65,82,
   115,119,233,244,186,172,112,85,6,56,38,44,85,72,32,47,63,96,124,
   217,314,319,221,644,817,921,934,922,416,275,10,22,18,46,127,181,
   101,39,86,183,116,139,164,212,218,296,815,380,412,460,495,675,820,
   932.

230

Lynchburg, Va., January 5th, 1822.

Dear Mr. Morriss.—You will find in one of the papers, written in cipher, the names of all my associates, who are each entitled to an equal part of our treasure, and opposite to the names of each one will be found the names and residences of the relatives and others, to whom they devise their respective portions. From this you will be enabled to carry out the wishes of all, by distributing the portion of each to the parties designated. This will not be difficult, as their residences are given, and they can easily be found.

The two letters given above were all the box contained that were intelligible ; the others, consisted of papers closely covered with figures, which were, of course, unmeaning until they could be deciphered. To do this was the task to which I now devoted myself, and with but partial success.

To enable my readers to understand the paper numbered "2," the Declaration of Independence is given, by the assistance of which its hidden meaning was made plain :

DECLARATION   INDEPENDENCE.

1. 2 3   4   5   6   9   10
When, in the course of human events it becomes necessary for one people to dissolve the political bands which have (20) connected them with another; and to assume among the powers (30) of the earth, the separate and equal station to which (40) the laws of nature and of nature's God entitle them, (50) a decent respect to the opinions of mankind requires that (60) they should declare the causes which impel them to the (70) separation.

We hold these truths to be self-evident, that (80) all men are created equal : that they are endowed by (90) their Creator with certain inalienable rights : that among these are (100) life, liberty, and the pursuit of happiness : that to secure (110) their rights, governments are instituted among men, deriving their just (120) powers from the consent of the governed : that when any (130) form of government becomes destructive of these ends, it is (140) the right of the people to alter or to abolish (150) it, and to institute a new government, laying its foundation (160) on such principles and organizing its powers in such form, (170) as to them shall seem most likely to effect their (180) safety and happiness. Prudence, indeed, will dictate that governments long (190) established, should not be changed for light and transient causes ; (200) and accordingly all experience hath shown that mankind are more (210) disposed to suffer, while evils are sufferable, than to right (220) themselves by abolishing the forms to which they are accustomed. (230) But, when a long train of abuses and usurpations, pursuing (240) invariably the same object, evinces a design to reduce them under (250) absolute despotism, it is their right, it is their duty, (260) to throw off such government, and to provide new guards (270) for their future security. Such has been the patient sufferance (280) of these colonies, and such is now the necessity which (290) constrains them to alter their former systems of government. The (300) history of the present King of

231

Great Britain is a (310) history of repeated injuries and usurpations, all having in direct (320) object the establishment of an absolute tyranny over these States. (330) To prove this, let facts be submitted to a candid (340) world.

He has refused his assent to laws the most (350) wholesome and necessary for the public good. He has forbidden (360) his governors to pass laws of immediate and pressing importance, (370) unless suspended in their operation till his assent should be (380) obtained; and when so suspended he has utterly neglected to (390) attend to them.

He has refused to pass other laws (400) for the accommodation of large districts of people, unless these (410) people would relinquish their right of representation in the legislature, (420) a right inestimable to them and formidable to tyrants only. (430)

He has called together legislative bodies at places unusual, uncomfortable (440) and distant from the depositary of their public records, for (450) the sole purpose of fatiguing them into compliance with his (460) measures.

He has dissolved representative houses repeatedly for opposing with (470) manly firmness, his invasions on the rights of the people. (480)

He has refused, for a long time after such dissolutions, (490) to cause others to be elected; whereby the legislative powers (490) incapable of annihilation, have returned to the people at large (500) for their exercise, the State remaining, in the meantime, (510) exposed to all the danger of invasion from without, and (520) convulsions within.

He has endeavored to prevent the population of (530) these States, for that purpose, obstructing the laws of naturalization (540) of foreigners; refusing to pass others to encourage their migration (550) hither, and raising the conditions of new appropriations of lands. (560)

He has obstructed the administration of justice by refusing his (570) assent to laws for establishing judiciary powers.

He has made (580) judges dependent on his will alone for the tenure of (590) their offices, and the amount and payment of their salaries. (600)

He has erected a multitude of new offices, and sent (610) hither swarms of officers to harass our people and eat (620) out their substance.

He has kept among us in times (630) of peace standing armies, without the consent of our legislature.

He (640) has offered to render the military independent of and superior (650) to the civil power.

He has combined with others to (660) subject us to a jurisdiction foreign to our constitution, and (670) unacknowledged by our laws, giving his assent to their acts of (680) pretended legislation.

For quartering large bodies of armed troops among (690) us;

For protecting them, by a mock trial, from punishment, (700) for any murders which they should commit on the inhabitants (710) of these States;

For cutting off our trade with all (720) parts of the world;

For imposing taxes on us without (730) our consent;

For depriving us, in many cases, of the (740) benefits of trial by jury;

For transporting us beyond seas (750) to be tried for pretended offences;

232

For abolishing the free (760) system of English laws in a neighboring province, establishing therein (770) an arbitrary government, and enlarging its boundaries so as to (780) render it, at once, an example and fit instrument for (790) introducing the same absolute rule in these colonies :

For taking (800) away our charters, abolishing our most valuable laws and altering (810) fundamentally, (811) the (812) powers (813) of (814) our (815) governments ; (816)

For suspending our own legislatures, and declaring themselves invested with power to legislate for us in all cases, whatsoever.

He has abdicated government here, by declaring us out of his protection, and waging war against us.

He has plundered our seas, ravaged our coasts, burnt our towns, and destroyed the lives of our people.

He is, at this time, transporting large armies of foreign mercenaries to complete the works of death, desolation and tyranny, already begun, with circumstances of cruelty and perfidy, scarcely paralleled in the most barbarous ages, and totally unworthy the head of a civilized nation.

He has constrained our fellow-citizens, taken captive on the high seas, to bear arms against their country, to become the executioners of their friends and brethren, or to fall themselves by their hands.

He has excited domestic insurrections amongst us, and has endeavored to bring on the inhabitants of our frontiers, the merciless Indian savages, whose known rule of warfare is an undistinguished destruction of all ages, sexes and conditions.

In every stage of these oppressions, we have petitioned for redress in the most humble terms ; our repeated petitions have been answered only by repeated injury. A prince, whose character is thus marked by every act which may define a tyrant, is unfit to be the ruler of a free people.

Nor have we been wanting in attention to our British brethren. We have warned them, from time to time, of attempts made by their legislature to extend an unwarrantable jurisdiction over us. We have reminded them of the circumstances of our emigration and settlement here. We have appealed to their native justice and magnanimity, and we have conjured them, by the ties of our common kindred, to disavow these usurpations, which would inevitably interrupt our connection and correspondence. They, too, have been deaf to the voice of justice and consanguinity.

We must, therefore, acquiesce in the necessity, which denounces our separation, and hold them, as we hold the rest of mankind, enemies in war—in peace, friends.

We, therefore, the representatives of the United States of America, in general congress assembled, appealing to the Supreme Judge of the world for the rectitude of our intentions, do, in the name, and by the authority of the good people of these Colonies, solemnly publish and declare, that these United Colonies are, and of right, ought to be, free and independent States ; that they are absolved from all allegiance to the British crown, and that all political connection between them and the State of Great Britain is, and ought to be, totally dissolved and that, as free and independent States, they have full power to levy war, conclude peace, contract alliances, establish commerce, and to do all other acts and things which independent states may of right do. And for the support of this declaration, with a firm reliance on the protection of Divine Providence, we mutually pledge to each other our lives, our fortunes, and our sacred honor.

The Psychology of the Ciphers: Key Figures

Colonel Fabyan, the great authority on codes, said of the Beale ciphers, "the psychology of it is about all we have to go on in picking out our point of attack," so let us sum up what we know of each of the key figures in the story going backwards from the known to the unknown in the hope of discovering new points of attack.

GEORGE HART, SR.—who put together the story of the Beale Treasure which is in the Roanoke Library, was a wonderful Virginia gentleman. The authors knew him well and respected him greatly. In his early years Mr. Hart lived in Roanoke, Virginia, coming to Washington, D.C., in 1919. Mr. Hart was a court stenographer and recorder and was used to careful, accurate reporting. Anything he did was done with meticulous care.

Mr. Hart was scrupulously honest. He was kindly but very straightforward in his manner. He called a spade a spade and would not knowingly mislead anyone.

George Hart told P. B. Innis that he was in favor of finding the key to the codes and proceeding from there rather than going and digging at random. He was against damaging property and, when his brother Clayton took dynamite to blow up a tree hoping to find the treasure underneath, he would have nothing to do with it.

George Hart knew N. H. Hazelwood, the man who gave the sheets of paper to Clayton to copy. He told P. B. Innis that Hazelwood and Clayton worked in the same office and it was Hazelwood who told Clayton about James B. Ward and the Job Print Pamphlet. Clayton Hart obtained a copy from James Ward but George did not have chance to study it thoroughly until after he moved to D.C. By this time Clayton was using other means and ideas to find the treasure.

In 1924 George sent the pamphlet to Colonel Fabyan hoping that he would be able to decipher it. The pamphlet was never returned and as far as George understood from Colonel Fabyan, he had not been able to decipher it and doubted if anyone could without the key.

CLAYTON HART—brother of George, lived and died in Roanoke. For some years he worked as a stenographer in the office of the Norfolk and Western railroad in that town. He was a shrewd, miserly man with an eccentric manner who kept to himself. Money was very important to Clayton and he would not spend a single cent if he could avoid it. Clayton never married, he considered a wife an unnecessary expense.

Clayton was distrustful. He considered that most people were out for themselves and didn't believe anything or anyone until he had checked out the details for himself. Although Hazelwood was one of his few friends, Clayton went to see James B. Ward himself to ask about the treasure and the pamphlet and check out Hazelwood's story.

Clayton did everything he could to check and recheck the treasure tale and, according to George Hart, he believed it all except for the way in which Beale and his party obtained the gold and silver. Clayton was sure that Beale was involved with the Cherokee Indians and their removal and resettlement. Between the years 1817 and the end of the 1820's, negotiations were almost constantly going on between these Indians and the United States. This, of course, was the time that Beale left Big Lick and was reportedly digging the gold and silver, coming back twice to hide it.

Clayton believed that the treasure, especially as it contained jewels, was bribe money for the tribal chiefs. As Beale and Morriss were friends with many important people, this was plausible. Beale wanted to keep his real reason for travelling West secret so, according to Clayton, he invented the story about hunting and trading.

Bribery was a more or less accepted method of gaining the assent of the tribal chiefs, often at the expense of the members of their own tribe. Clayton thought that Beale kept back treasure for himself and, when the Indians found out, they killed him and all his men.

Clayton spent much time researching Indian records and left many notes regarding this. However, George Hart said, "Clayton did not get anywhere."

There are a number of flaws in this story of Clayton's which will be discussed later.

N. H. HAZELWOOD — this is the forgotten man, overlooked by most researchers even though he is a key figure in this treasure hunt. Hazelwood was chief clerk to the auditor of the Norfolk and Western railroad, Roanoke, Virginia, where Clayton Hart worked as a stenographer.

In the summer of 1897, Hazelwood asked Clayton to make several copies of eight sheets of notepaper. 2 sheets headed simply, no. 1. 3 sheets headed no. 2. 3 sheets headed no. 3.

It is important to note that these were SHEETS of paper, not pages of a pamphlet. They were handwritten, not printed. Noticing that the sheets of paper were very different from the usual work he was given to type, Clayton asked Hazelwood what they were all about. Hazelwood said the papers were connected with a treasure said to have been buried about 80 years earlier near the foot of the Peaks of Otter close to his home.

Hazelwood said Clayton could keep a copy of the papers for himself. They worked together on the codes for sometime but neither of them did any good. Then, when Hazelwood's health began to fail, he told Clayton to go ahead on his own.

Hazelwood at this time revealed to Clayton that a man named James B. Ward of Lynchburg had deciphered one of the codes and had printed a pamphlet on the subject.

Hazelwood said that he tried to persuade Ward not to publish the pamphlet because the treasure belonged to the descendants of Beale's party and was not his to give away. Ward, however, needed money so badly that he went ahead with the project saying that he would make a few changes so no one could decipher the codes. But the printing establishment was burned down before the pamphlet could be distributed. Hazelwood believed this was done by a relative of one of the party to prevent other people from getting the treasure. Hazelwood said people got wind of the pamphlet and its contents from workers in the printing shop.

To stop any more trouble Hazelwood got the original papers from Ward so he could not reprint. George Hart said that after Clayton typed the codes he handed back the original 8 sheets of paper to Hazelwood together with the typed copies. The sheets of paper were in a bad shape from first Morriss and then Ward working on them for so many years. This was why Hazelwood wanted them typed.

The fact that Thomas J. Beale refers to SHEETS of paper in the box and Robert Morriss speaks of the SHEETS of paper covered with figures and James Ward mentions Morriss giving him the box containing SHEETS of paper, makes it almost certain that the SHEETS of paper Hazelwood gave to Clayton to type were Beale's own codes.

It is these codes from the sheets of paper that are given in this book on pages

JAMES B. WARD—Some new material collected by the authors clarifies the picture of this man who received a great deal of attention from researchers and treasure hunters. The possibility that Ward made up the whole story to make some money has been investigated. Because no copy of the original pamphlet was available, many people refused to believe a pamphlet ever existed and thought that the whole story was made up by the Harts or the Innises in spite of the fact that George Hart had sent a copy to Colonel Fabyan, and Walter Innis's Bedford County relative had a copy some years ago.

Lynchburg, Va., March 26th 1884

27

A. R. Spofford
Librarian of Congress.

Dr Sir

I am informed that to secure the copy right of a book, all that is necessary, is to send you a copy, written or printed, of the title page with one dollar, and you will give the requisite protection. A copy of the book itself, to be sent you when printed. Presuming this to be so, I enclose you one dollar and the following copy of the title page.

The Beale Papers

Containing authentic statements in regard to the treasure buried in 1819, and 1821, near Bufords, in Bedford County, Virginia, and which has never been recovered.

Price 50 cts.

Please enter in my name as agent for the author. Trusting to hear from you at your earliest convenience.

I am Respectfully,
Yr Obt Svt
Jas. B. Ward.

239

𝕷ibrary of 𝕮ongress, to wit: No. 7558

Be it Remembered, That on the *31* day of *March*
anno domini 1885, *James B. Ward*
.... of *Lynchburgh, Va*
.... ha*s* deposited in this office the title o
  Book ....the title or descript
of which is in the following words, to wit:

The Beale Papers,
Containing authentic Statements
regarding the Treasure buried in
1819 and 1821 near Bufords, in
Bedford County, Virginia, and
which has never been recovered

Lynchburgh
1885

The right whereof *he*   claim*s* as proprietor   in conformity with
the laws of the United States respecting Copyrights

A. R. Spofford
                                                Librarian of Congress.

.... of the above publication deposited   , 188

240

Finding evidence that James B. Ward was granted copyright in 1885 for his pamphlet entitled *The Beale Papers* proved to the Innises that James B. Ward and his pamphlet existed at one time.

No copy was found in the copyright office, but Frank Aaron found a letter from Ward to the Library of Congress enquiring about copyright. This letter is dated March 26, 1884. This proves that the pamphlet was written before that date and that neither the Harts or the Innises fabricated it.

This letter tells us a great deal about Ward. The handwriting is good and clear. The spelling is correct and the language that of an educated man. As the address on the letter is Lynchburg, Virginia, it confirms he was living in the area at the time.

There is a lapse of a year between James B. Ward's letter of application and the granting of the copyright. This could have been due to delays in postal delivery and arranging the details of publication. However, it could have been due to Hazelwood's efforts in dissuading Ward from publishing it at all, or from Ward deciding to alter the text and make changes in the codes.

It is interesting to note that while a fee of one dollar was paid and the title page duly sent and acknowledged, the copyright certificate shows no record of an actual copy being received.

Although the pamphlet states that Ward intended to use an agent to spare him all the enquiries and harassments which might follow the publication of the pamphlet and even describes this agent as a man known to himself and Morriss, the copyright application shows Ward asking to be named as his own agent.

Was Hazelwood the man he hoped would act as agent? And, when Hazelwood objected to the publication, did Ward decide to be his own agent?

The title Ward gives the pamphlet in his letter to the Librarian of Congress is:

THE BEALE PAPERS

Containing Authentic Statements regarding the Treasure buried in 1819 and 1821 near Bufords' in Bedford County,

Virginia, and which has never been recovered
Price Fifty Cents

— — — —

Lynchburg:
Virginian Book and Job Print,
1885

(Fifty cents was a large sum in 1885.)

Ward never gave the name of the person he had selected to act as agent in publishing and circulating *The Beale Papers,* but it was in his house that Mrs. Morriss died. If Sarah Mitchell Morriss's death certificate or notice could be found, it could be very helpful. Was she related to the Mitchell Wagon family?

Clayton Hart visited Ward on two occasions and found him living in Lynchburg in very simple surroundings. The fact that his circumstances deteriorated steadily bears out Ward's own story that he had wasted his life on the codes and allowed his business and his family to suffer. Clayton also met James Ward's son who worked on the railroad and who also lived in humble circumstances. If Ward had found the treasure as Colonel Fabyan suggested, surely he would have used the money to make himself more comfortable.

As can be seen from the letterhead of Ward's letter to the Librarian of Congress, he was writing from the Office of Adams Bros and Payne Feed Store, Twelfth Street, near Main, Lynchburg. This office was the headquarters for feed of all kinds as well as for Ship Stuff, Brown Stuff, etc. In addition they were agents for Mitchell Farm Wagons and Freight Wagons and for Watertown Spring Wagons and Buggies. Mrs. Morriss's maiden name was Sarah Mitchell, by the way.

Was Ward working in this store when his letter requesting copyright was written in 1884? We know that some 20 years earlier Ward was in comfortable circumstances, having $10,000 of taxable property. This included a farm. Probably he bought seed and feed from Adams Bros then. As the years passed he paid less and less tax, which suggests that he had less and less income coming in.

James B. Ward is said to be of good ancestry, being related to the Edward Ward who, in 1821, was a candidate for the governorship of Tennessee. Edward Ward is described as coming from Virginia and his opponents said he was a Federalist whose 'Virginia bearing, affluence and social position made him unacceptable to frontiersmen.' Several inhabitants of Bedford, Virginia, were supporters of Edward Ward, but Andrew Erwin, a land speculator and planter of Bedford country, was against him and his great friend Andrew Jackson.

Ward Gap in the Blue Ridge mountains is named for this family of Wards.

The fact that Robert Morriss, who gave the Beale box and papers to James B. Ward, knew most of the great people of the day and, among his guests and devoted personal friends, were Andrew Jackson, Clay, Coles, Chief Justice Marshall and a host of others, suggests that the Ward family including James B. Ward may have known some of these important people over the years.

Furthermore, an advertisement was put in the Lynchburg papers in 1832 by A. Hatcher offering the Washington Tavern for sale with the condition that one Seth Ward remain in residence until he died.

The Beale papers pamphlet corroborates this. On page 6, it says about Robert Morriss, 'there are those living who will testify to the fact that he permitted a boarder, in no way connected with him, to remain in the house for more than 20 years, and until he died without even receiving the slightest remuneration and that he was never made to feel otherwise than as a favored guest.'

Was Seth Ward a relative of James B. Ward? Seth was an older man and may have known Beale and something of his plans.

To sum up, it appears that James B. Ward's description of himself and his work on the codes as given in the pamphlet, is true. Also it appears to be true that he was of good family, but gave so much time to the codes that he became poverty-stricken and exhausted. It seems very believable that he wrote the pamphlet to raise some desperately needed money and that he never found the treasure.

Did he alter the codes as Hazelwood said? Or did Robert Morriss do this before he gave them to him?

This is discussed on page

ROBERT MORRISS — Born 1778 in the state of Maryland; Married 1803 to Miss Sarah Mitchell in Loudon County, Va.; Widowed 1861; Died Saturday, Jan. 3, 1863. Notice of death in Lynchburg papers Jan. 8, 1863, placed by niece Rosalyn, Mrs. David Saunders.

Robert Morriss is the only link we have back to Thomas Jefferson Beale. Was Morriss the perfect, honest gentleman that is described in the pamphlet and in Beale's letters? Or was he the villain of the whole piece?

Did Robert Morriss himself find the treasure and pass on the box with altered codes to Ward to cover up his perfidy? Morriss seemed to have lived very comfortably and it is hard to believe that he would have completely forgotten the box, particularly as he moved more than once and would have had to take the box with him.

Furthermore, J. Solario of the Brookings Institution discovered that the St. Louis Beacon of August 1832, exactly ten years after Beale left the box with Morriss, printed a notice saying that the Post Office was holding a letter for Robert Morriss.

Was this the missing key?

In his letter of 1822 Beale says that Morriss is to open the box after ten years and the key will be sent to him in 1832. It would be a remarkable coincidence if a letter was left for another

Robert Morriss whose name was spelled exactly the same way, at the St. Louis Post Office exactly the same year as Beale promised!

The Innises have spent a great deal of time and trouble trying to trace this letter. Was it picked up by Morriss? Did someone pick it up for him? Was it thrown in the trash?

In 1832 travellers from the West would often carry letters from the inhabitants of places they would pass through on their journey. Recipients would gladly pay them a fee for this service. It is possible that some traveller carried the letter to Morriss.

No one knows what happened to letters not picked up or claimed at the Post Office in those days. No records were kept and there is no way of knowing if Robert Morriss ever received this letter.

The St. Louis Beacon started publication in 1832 and ended in 1839 and has no other record of Morriss except notice of this letter. Eleanor McCarthy of St. Louis kindly researched various records in St. Louis and found that Elias Rector was Postmaster in 1821, Wilson Hunt was Postmaster in 1836 and 37 and, although there is mention of one Wilson Burns as Postmaster in 1832, no record has been found of him.

The Innises checked and found no record of Robert Morriss travelling from Lynchburg to St. Louis by boat or other public conveyance.

All that is printed or written about Robert Morriss says that he was an honest, kind and compassionate gentleman beloved by all who knew him. It is said, as mentioned earlier, that many of the great men of the day were his friends and guests. If all this is true, then Robert Morriss would not have acted in bad faith and we must believe that the story he told to Ward is true and that the person who wrote the codes and the letters and gave them in the box to Robert Morriss was Thomas Jefferson Beale.

THOMAS JEFFERSON BEALE — Who was he? There are many persons named Beale. Several called Thomas Beale and even Thomas Jefferson Beale. The name Beale was sometimes spelled Beall or Bealle. In those days there are many variations in the spelling of the same name. There are famous families of Beales and Bealls in Maryland and Virginia, but so far, there is no way of definitely proving that the Thomas Jefferson Beale of the Beale Treasure is linked to any one of them. We still do not know for certain if our Thomas Jefferson Beale ever existed. We have to take Morris's word for it.

Robert Morriss says he appeared to be a gentleman with a free and independent air. He was sociable and friendly and popular with the ladies. Beale was six feet tall with jet black hair and eyes. His hair was worn rather long. Robert Morriss says that his complexion was swarthy as if he spent a lot of time in the open air. He was strong and active. Altogether, says Morriss, he was a model of manly beauty, favored by the ladies and envied by the men. Morriss had the impression that Beale came from the western part of the state.

From Beale's letters we know that he was an educated man, probably a military person who had a knowledge of surveying as well as military matters. Like most gentlemen of that day, he was most likely a Mason, possibly of the Scottish rite.

Clayton Hart's belief that Beale was involved with the Cherokees' removal and resettlement is plausible, but it may have been that Beale was acting for them behind the scenes trying to get a better bargain for them. The Indians could have shown him where to find the gold and silver in return for his help and, when the terms were not to their liking, perhaps they did kill him and all his party.

Treaties were made with the Cherokees in 1817, 1818 and 1819. Thomas Jefferson, as early as 1803, had suggested that Indians living east of Mississippi be moved to the Louisiana Purchase. Tennesseans liked this idea as they wanted to move out the Indians. Many Cherokees did not want to go West and there was trouble.

It is interesting to note that the name of one Captain Thos. J. Beall from Harpers Ferry, common passenger, is on the muster roll of the ship Synia which was voyaging to New Orleans in 1816. (see illustration page 248 . This note appears in

JOURNAL from BOSTON to the WESTERN COUNTRY and down the OHIO and MISSISSIPPI RIVERS to NEW ORLEANS, by
WILLIAM RICHARDSON.

The muster roll appears on page 248 and there are other references to Capt. Beall on pages 31 and 34 of the journal.

Was this our man Beale going to take a look before taking his party West in 1817?

Land was up for grabs in the West and veterans were being encouraged to settle. Was Beale looking for settlement land for himself and party? Or as he said himself, was he hunting and looking for a good trading post as other men were doing so successfully? Or, as Clayton Hart thought, was Beale looking over the possibilities for Cherokee settlement in Louisiana?

We cannot say at this point, but we do know that Beale knew the area around Bufords, Lynchburg and Big Lick, as Roanoke was then called. The facts are that he returned twice and chose to bury the treasure in this area because as he said, all the party were familiar with it.

When Beale wrote the codes we know he used the Declaration of Independence as the key to one of them at least. It is likely that he used other documents of his friend and namesake Thomas Jefferson.

Even though he was President of the United States, only 3 things are mentioned on Jefferson's tombstone just as Jefferson himself requested. These are that he was the

Author of the Declaration of Independence
Of the Statute of Virginia for Religious Freedom and
Father of the University of Virginia.

Muster Roll of Boat Synia[13].

Major Daniel Halliday, Captain & one (of) the Com. for internal regulation of Miss. Territory

William Richardson — Captain & Treasurer of Boston

Stephen Donohoe — one of Com. for internal reg^n & has charge of the spirits, Alexandria, Virg.

Walter Nash Do Do — & one of the managers in the cooking depart., Miss Ter^y

Henry Burt Esqre Trader, from N. York

Maj^r Nelson, assistant to cooking department — Pennsylvania

Capt. Thos. J. Beall common pass — from Harper's Ferry

Henry Wilkins Do Do — Pittsburg

Mount Do — Alexandria, Virginia

Doct^r L. S. Parmeley Do Do — Boston, Mass.

Mr. McAdams — Steersman

Morris — Oarsman

Stone — Do

Bill — Do

Lewis — Do

Limerick — Cook — black — belonging to Maj^r Halliday

Daniel Boy — Do — belonging to Nash

---

17 Persons

Jefferson was the 3rd President of the United States. It is therefore possible that Beale used these 3 documents as keys to his 3 codes.

As Beale was staying in Lynchburg when he wrote part of the codes, one would think he would use the official copy of the Declaration which had been approved by the signers. This is the copy shown in this book on page 231. It is scarcely likely that he would have taken the liberty to change any words or to number the words of the Declaration incorrectly. Although there is the possibility that he may have done this to mislead people.

Whatever his intentions, we know that Thomas Jefferson Beale was a very clever man and probably the only person to write a code which the C.I.A. cannot break.

Stage road

public road

ORIGINAL IN Library Congress

MADISON MAP 1809

Madison's Map Sheds New Light
on the Beale Treasure

by P.B. Innis Copyright 1984.

Of great importance to Beale Treasure Hunters is a map of Virginia made by Bishop James Madison in 1807. This is recognized as the best map of the time until Herman Boyer produced his map in 1826.

Madison's map was updated and corrected in 1818 and sold for ten dollars.

This map is of great value to Beale treasure Hunters because it shows the landmarks Beale mentions in his letters and also those mentioned in code 2.

Buford's Inn is shown, also the north and south forks of Goose Creek as well as the early roads which went west and through the Blue Ridge.

A comparison with other early maps reveals important differences in the position of these roads and of Buford's Inn. This could considerably affect our calculations regarding the Treasure site. Also the date when the Black Horse Tavern was in existence.

Beale tells us in code number two, the only one of the three codes which has been deciphered, that he and his companions buried the treasure about four miles from Budord's, therefore, the Inn's exact location is of great importance in locating the Treasure Vault.

Madison's Map places Buford's Inn further west than the old chimney which still stands behind the present brick building in Montvale. As we have spent a great deal of time and money searching for the Treasure and have based our calculations on the old chimney site, we were very concerned to find this difference.

However, we are glad to discover any new clues which will help prove or disprove the facts given by Beale and which may lead us to the Treasure at last. But we realize that even though Madison was a Bishop, first cousin of the President and head of William and Mary college, he could make a mistake.

Could Madison have made a mistake in placing the Buford's further west? Were there two buildings at that time? On Madison's Map the building is coded as a "House of Entertainment" and this made us wonder if it were a Playhouse or a House of Ill Fame. But when we looked it up in a dictionary of archaic terms, we found that a "House of Entertainment" in those days, meant a "Place of Refreshment for Man and Beast." In other words an Inn or Tavern.

It was unlikely that there would be two Inns so close together at the same time. Did Madison place the Inn in the wrong place on his map? After all he was not a cartographer.

After much research we came across a map of Bedford County circa 1819 and, to our astonishment, this map showed not ONE but THREE buildings known as Bufords!

More research revealed that the most westward building was the same as the "House of Entertainment" shown on Madison's Map. The middle building was probably the one marked by the old chimney still standing today, and then the third building is coded on the map as a mill. This mill was south east of the present building.

All of these buildings were known as Budord's and the tract of land on which all these three were standing, was called Budord's also. (It was later that part of the tract was named Locust Level.)

These maps raised several questions. We have been using the old chimney as the center from which we measured the four mile radius where we search for the Treasure. Should we be using the west building? Or perhaps the Mill? Just a few feet can make a lot of difference when digging for treasure and so we began trying to discover which building had been the Inn where Beale an his party lodged in 1819 and 1821.

Madison's map showed the road going west through Buford's Gap and on through Salem. It also showed another road going west from Fincastle and joining up with the lower road not far from Salem. There was no road marked on this map over the Blue Ridge from Fincastle to Montvale. Therefore the Black Horse Tavern would not have been built at the time Beale buried the Treasure as there would have been no use for it.

Because the road over the mountain was not marked on Madison's Map when it was updated and corrected in 1817, we think the center building marked by the old chimney, was not used as an Inn until the road over the mountain was built and used by the stage coach. While it is possible that there was a trail over the Blue Ridge, it was certainly not a well used road or it would have been marked on the Madison Map.

The west building was the first built by the Buford family and as it was directly on the old road to and from the west, this is most probably where Beale lodged. The center building, where the old chimney still stands, most likely became the Inn, later, when the Fincastle coach started coming over the mountain. This would be the most convenient place to stop for refreshment for man and beast and to pick up or drop off passengers coming or going to other destinations.

The old west building probably fell into disuse when the stage coach route changed. So far, we have not discovered the foundations of the old west building or the mill.

Another important feature of the Madison map is that longitude is given west of Washington, not of the Greenwich Meridian as is usually done. This could make some difference in the calculation of distance

Is Fisher Digging in the Wrong Place?

by P.B. Innis

Beale Treasure hunters all over the country were excited to hear that the world famous treasure hunter, Mel Fisher, had deserted the sea and is now in Montvale, Virginia, hunting for the Beale treasure. Fisher and his partner, Gordon Klemme, have bought up five acres of land not far from the present Buford's Inn and they are putting most of their effort around Graham's Mill on Goose Creek.

For several reasons which we give below, we think that Fisher is digging in the wrong place.

The Beale treasure was buried on two separate occasions by Thomas Jefferson Beale and his companions who found the gold and silver in the mountains north of Santa Fe in 1818. The treasure was brought back and buried within a four mile radius of Buford's Tavern and then Beale and his company went back for more but never returned.

However, Beale had left a box with a friend, Robert Morriss, and told him to open it after ten years if he did not come back. When, at last, Morriss opened the box he found some letters written by Beale and several papers covered with numbers. A piece of scrap paper with some numbers on it was also in the box.

The code which describes the treasure has been deciphered using the Declaration of Independence as the key. This code says that one of the three papers tells exactly where the treasure is buried, one describes the treasure in detail and the third gives the names of the next kin of the members of Beale's party.

For many years all kinds of people have been trying to decipher the other two codes. We, ourselves, managed to decipher a little of the code telling where the treasure was hidden, and we gave the results of this in the front of the 1981 edition of our book *Gold in the Blue Ridge*. Unfortunately, this wasn't enough for us to find the treasure. Even though we have dug eleven times, all we have found is an old wagon wheel!

Fisher, who says he has deciphered part of the codes, believes that Beale dammed up Goose Creek above the mill, dug down in the creek bed, buried the first load of treasure and then allowed the creek to run back over it. He and his partners believe the second load was buried close by.

We think this is unlikely because we did a study of the rainfall in November 1819 when Beale says they buried the first load and found that there was heavy rainfall that month and no frost. This means that the creek would be exceptionally full and the land around would be soft and wet, making it very difficult to haul a heavy load of gold and silver anywhere except on a hard surface. Further more, it would take time to do the job as Fisher describes it, so surely someone would have seen what they were up to.

Another reason we feel Fisher may be in the wrong place is that since our last dig which was not far from where he is now digging, we found two old maps which shed new light on the treasure area.

In 1807, Bishop James Madison, President of William and Mary College and a cousin of President Madison, produced a map of Virginia and updated it in 1818. This map was considered the best map of Virginia until Herman Boyer made another in 1826.

Madison's map shows the landmarks mentioned by Beale in his letters and also those mentioned in code 2. Buford's Inn is shown but it is placed further west than we expected. It is located in Buford's Gap right on the boundary line between Botetourt and Beford Counties. This is some distance further west than the old chimney which we thought was where Beale and his party lodged when they buried the first treasure load. This is an important difference because Beale said the treasure is hidden within a four mile radius of Buford's and calculations would be wrong unless the correct building is used.

Should we have been using the site of the "house of entertainment?" Or perhaps, the mill?

No name is given this mill but it is doubtful that Graham's Mill where Fisher is digging was in existence in 1819 and can be the old mill which was on the Buford tract.

Yet another reason why Mel Fisher may be digging in the wrong place is the important evidence of N. H. Hazelwood, the man overlooked by most Beale treasure hunters. Hazelwood who, in 1897, brought the sheets of paper from the box to Clayton Hart, a stenographer of the Norfolk and Western Railroad, and asked him to copy them. Altogether there were 8 sheets of paper, two headed "no 1"; three headed " no 2"; and three sheets headed "no 3". These were sheets of paper, not pages from the pamphlet. They were handwritten, not printed, so they must have been the original sheets from the box.

Noticing that the sheets of paper were just a collection of numbers, Clayton asked Hazelwood what they were about. Hazelwood told him they were connected with a treasure buried 80 years earlier near the foot of the Peaks of Otter not far from his home. It is interesting to note that there is a mill marked on Map 2 near the base of the Peaks of Otter on the north fork of Goose Creek.

This was told to me by George Hart, Senior, Clayton's brother, who also knew Hazelwood personally. Both brothers spent years looking for the treasure without any luck.

Since I wrote the first article on the Beale treasure in 1964 and then the book, Gold in the Blue Ridge, many people have contacted us saying they have deciphered the codes and know exactly where the treasure is hidden, but, so far, it has not been unearthed.

Mr. John Luck, now age 90, a forest ranger who has lived in Montvale all his life and knew Walter Innis when he was a boy camping on the Peaks of Otter looking for the treasure, thinks the gold and silver is hidden on his property. Several small treasure finds have occurred on his land, but not the Beale treasure. Mr. Fisher has the money, the tenacity and the veracity needed to solve the mystery, so may be if he keeps searching, he will be the lucky one, but he'd better look out, we are getting ready to dig again ourselves!

August 13, 1964
Washington, D.C.

Dear Alma and Bert:

Rear Admiral Walter D. Innis, USN, Retired, and his wife may
motor to Roanoke some time soon, where he visited as a young man, a
while there she would like to look up any new information about what
call The Beale Treasure. She wrote the piece in the August issue of
Argosy, from my record.

I wish you would give her an opportunity to see Clayton's reco
of what he and I and others did to try to find the treasure, and you can
depend upon her being square, not like the man and woman who recen
visited you.

I hope you and Bert are quite well, and with all good wishes,

Cordially yours,
Zernie.

To Mr. & Mrs. J. R. Keyser,
Roanoke.

Dear Mrs. Innes:

I have written a letter, of which this is a copy, to my youngest
sister and her husband, in Roanoke, Va. and inasmuch as she insists on
getting all her mail in her post office box, I don't find a record of her
residence in Southeast Roanoke, but you can get it from the telephone
directory. Don't forget to go to the Roanoke Public Library. They have
photostated copy of my record, and I understand are furnishing it to
inquirers, I do not know at what price.

With all good wishes,
Geo. L. Hart, Sr.

September 19, 1964
Washington, D.C.

Dear Mrs. Innis:

  I regret very much that my youngest sister, who grabbed Clayton's records of his half-century hunt for the Beale treasure, after he died, and I was not there when the division was made. I do not know that it would have helped you, but I should like for you to have seen that record.

  I enclose some data that I have had, and they will doubtless explain themselves.

  I have heard nothing from Geo. L. and Lou since they left with Zernie for Harvard University.

  With all good wishes,

    Cordially yours,
    Geo. L. Hart, Sr.

September 24, 1964
Washington, D.C.

Dear Mr. Spivey:

I have your interesting undated letter, and am forwarding it to Mrs. Innis, who wrote the article in the August number of *Argosy*. Mr Innis is the wife of Rear Admiral Walter D. Innis, USN, Retired. She and her husband are friends of my son, Judge George L. Hart, Jr. of the United States District Court of the District of Columbia.

She heard me tell of the efforts of my late brother Clayton and myself, I for 22 years until I moved form Roanoke, Va., to the District Columbia, and he until his death, which encompassed a period of 50 years. But we had no success.

I turned my record over to Mr. Barnes, at Roanoke, Va., who writes an article for the World-News, at Roanoke, every Saturday evening. He turned my record over to the Roanoke Public Library and they photostated it. And since Mrs. Innis' article appeared I understan they are selling copies for $16.75.

Inasmuch as my trip to Montvale, Bedford County, Virginia, (and the place was then known as Buford) was at night, I could not be any benefit to one hunting the treasure, for Clayton and I merely followed the guidance of the young man he had under hypnotism, who sa he could take us to the treasure. But we went where he guided us, and dug and dug, and found nothing. He was again hypnotized, and claime we were over too far, that he could see the gold, silver and jewels two feet to the left. It was then not far from daylight, and I, in disgust, pull up and we drove home. Clayton afterwards went down with dynamite, with which I would have no part, and blew out the tree and everything around it, but found no treasure.

I wish you luck, and I warn you that if you should break the co and find the treasure, you better protect yourself, and I cannot suggest how, or Uncle Sam, the Virginia authorities, and the owner of the land where the treasure is buried, will try to take almost all of it away from you. Clayton and I had planned, if we found the treasure, to leave it at hiding place, find out who owned the property, and try to purchase abo 10 acres of it for a summer home. I do not know whether this would have worked or not.

As I am now almost 91 years of age, I do not care to go into th matter further, and wish you luck.

Cordially yours,
(Geo. L. Hart, Sr.)

September 11, 1964
Washington, D.C.

Dear Mr. Mickle:

I have had before for a day or two your favor, without date, in regard to the Beale Fortune. My brother Clayton and I spent many years, I 20 and he near 40, trying to find a key to the code which tells where the gold, silver and jewels are buried. However, we never found that key. I am now past 90 years of age and am not disposed to work on it any more.

I was initiated into the Masonic order at Roanoke, VA., in 1919 just as I was pulling up stakes there and locating here in Washington, D.C.. I am also a member of Kazim Temple, Oranoke, Va. So I never had occasion to try to use any of the Masonic material, which you suggest may contain the key.

Now, it is possible that the material to be studied may be found in the Washington memorial, on shooters Hill, Alexandria, Va., or in the House of the Temple, on 16th street in this city. However, there are two reason why I do not look into that: (1) My age precludes my going to these places and spending hours, yes, days, trying to find the key; and, (2) there has been so much publicity there about my connection with this subject, that some of the people at those places would be sure to get onto what I was seeking, and possible go at it themselves. That would defeat your purpose. So I throw the subject back into your lap, and ask you to follow it as far as you see fit.

With all good wishes,

Cordially yours,
Geo. L. Hart, Sr.

Newspaper Notices re the BEALE Treasure

In addition to the notice appearing in the St. Louis Beacon of August 1832 in which the Post Office advertised that it was holding a letter for a Robert Morriss, the Lynchburg newspaper of April 10th 1885, reported the following:

TREASURE BURIED IN BEDFORD. A pamphlet under the title, *The Beale Papers*, has just made its appearance in the city and contains what are said to be authentic statements in regard to an immense treasure hidden in Bedford county near Bufords, by several miners in 1823. This information has been in the possession of a gentleman in this city for many years, but it has never before been made public. That gentleman has devoted much time working on the key which locates the pit where the treasure can be found, and has succeeded in getting points which will lead the reader to the place where the immense treasure is buried. He has been compelled to give the papers up and now all who purchase one of the books will have an opportunity to search for the big boxes of gold and silver now concealed. One of the papers states that the treasure consists of 2129 pounds of gold, 3120 pounds of silver and jewelry valued at 13,000$. Mr. J. B. Ward of the county will sell the books at 50 cents each to all who wish them.

Buy a book, get a pick and shovel, strike for Bufords, dig, grow rich or starve.

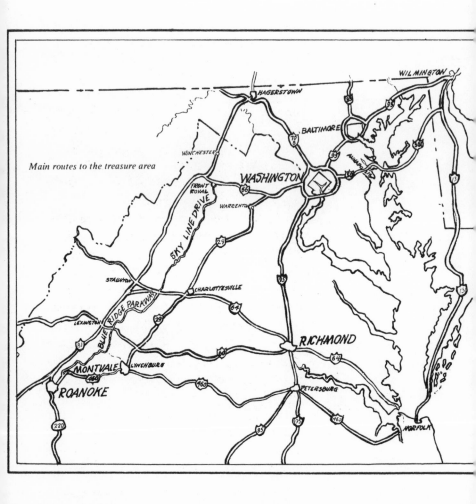

Main routes to the treasure area